Volume 12
MINING TECHNIQUES
PANTOGRAPH

The ILLUSTRATED
SCIENCE *and* INVENTION
ENCYCLOPEDIA

International Edition

H. S. STUTTMAN CO., INC. *publishers*   New York, N.Y. 10016

how it works

Published by H. S. STUTTMAN CO., Inc.
New York, N.Y. 10016
© Marshall Cavendish Limited 1974, 1976, 1977

MINING TECHNIQUES

In common with many other heavy engineering activities, mining is essentially a large scale exercise in material handling, although of a complexity much greater than in any other industry. Not only must large tonnages of mineral and ore be moved distances of up to ten miles (16 km) underground but also the circulation of ventilating air or the pumping of water can entail a vastly greater mass movement than the haulage of the rock. Indeed there are mines operating today where for every ton of mineral or ore brought to the surface, up to 20 tons of air have been circulated or up to 100 tons of water pumped out of the mine. The cost of providing adequate ventilation and drainage facilities may on occasion constitute a greater financial burden than the cost of breaking down the ore or mineral at the face.

History of mining Mining did not really begin until the start of the 'age of metals' some 5000 years ago, although some primitive mining activity had taken place during the long period of the Stone Age when Neolithic man exploited flint deposits, first on the surface and then underground. Some of these early flint mines consisted of vertical shafts up to 6 ft (2 m) in diameter sunk through the ground to a depth of 30 ft (10 m). From the foot of these shafts tunnels were driven somewhat haphazardly out into the deposit. Old mining implements included deerhorn picks and the shoulder blades of various large animals used as shovels.

The earliest records of organized mining operations are those of the Egyptians, dating from about 3000 BC. Mining for gold, silver, copper and turquoise was carried out on an appreciable scale, although most of these mining operations were confined to near-surface deposits. Probably the most

Above: hydraulic mining of tin in Malaya. Ore is washed out with water as a slurry, a method also used for china clay.

Below: workers, including children, at a Sicilian sulphur mine, c 1920. Although the modern Frasch process was already in use elsewhere, these crude hand tools (and caged canaries to test the air) could have been seen at any time since the Middle Ages.

graphic and harrowing account of ancient mining is that given by the Greek historian Diodorus Siculus, who visited Egypt in 50 BC, when he described the hapless plight of the thousands of prisoners labouring in the old underground gold mines on the Ethiopian border. In this description Siculus mentioned 'fire-setting'—the universal method at that time of driving tunnels through hard rock. Basically, fire-setting consisted of lighting brushwood fires against the solid face of the rock and then, when it was hot, rapidly cooling it by throwing cold water against the exposed face. This abrupt cooling had the desired effect of inducing cracks which enabled the rock to be broken down by primitive picks and wedges.

The next great race of people to advance the spread of mining were the Romans. Although not themselves miners, they had learned mining from the many different nations they had conquered, and consequently accumulated considerable experience which had been acquired in the course of centuries by many different races. The Romans mined on a large scale and evidence of their industry—or more correctly that of their slaves—is to be found throughout Europe and Africa. Mining continued following the collapse of the Roman empire and by the Middle Ages the metalliferous mining industry was strongly established in Europe. The famous book *De Re Metallica* by AGRICOLA, published in 1556, contains a complete account of mining at that time and may be considered to be the foundation of mining literature.

Steam power It was not until the advent of steam and the harnessing of this new source of power to ventilation, drainage and hoisting that any really significant developments in mining techniques were made. The industrial revolution of the 18th and 19th centuries brought about more progress in mining than had been achieved in the previous five millenia of mining history. These two centuries of development transformed mining from a relatively scattered and indiscriminate nibbling at the mineral wealth of the Earth's crust into a well planned and directed industry ranging over the entire world and of a complexity and scope never dreamed of by Agricola. This transformation did not take place without a heavy price being paid. As mines and mining became more complex so did the toll in human suffering, and the world's mining industry entered the present century with an estimated annual death toll of the order of 50,000. In the first half of the 20th century mechanization paved the way for booming production but replacement of men by machines was not always an unqualified blessing, and often this swing away from pick and shovel mining meant that the ancient rate was increased. Fortunately, stricter safety standards and improved machines and techniques introduced over the past several decades have brought about a significant improvement in overall safety. Despite the fact that the total yearly tonnage of mineral and ore now mined is several times greater than that produced at the beginning of the century, the world accident rate has been reduced by some 90%. Nevertheless mining is still inherently a dangerous occupation, and until such time as machines take over entirely from miners, a continuing price in human suffering is inevitable.

Quite apart from the overriding need to reduce the number of men at risk in mining operations, the high wages cost of labour in most mining areas has dictated the replacement of men by machines in the performance of mining operations. Equipment has been evolved which will win, load and transport minerals and ores with the minimum of manual attention.

Unfortunately, mining more than any other industry suffers

RAY DEAN

Left: the Bethesda slate quarry in North Wales. Slate is less in demand for roofing and similar uses than it used to be, but a lot is still mined. The typical terraced structure of an opencast mine results from the extraction of the mineral in sections of a convenient working depth, and makes it easier to build temporary roads to remove it by truck.

Right: aerial view of Mount Morgan mine, Queensland, Australia, which in 1973 produced 8488 metric tons of copper, 53,432 ounces of gold and 42,882 ounces of silver from 1.3 million tons of ore. Separation of the ores and smelting of metals are carried out at the mine itself, which reduces transport costs; much of the plant can be seen in the picture. The circular objects are settling tanks, which are also illustrated in the article on gold; in the foreground are the large heaps on to which waste from the operation is tipped. Large trucks transport ore and waste about the site.

from a fundamental lack of conformity both as regards processes and products and these widely varying conditions militate against straightforward application of standard automated processes. In no other industry is the problem of effective communication and control so acute, for there can be few industrial undertakings where the working area is spread over several square miles; where there are perhaps twenty or more widely scattered points of production, and where the entire operation cannot be readily observed and supervised. Fully automated mining coal face systems, however, are already in operation despite these difficulties and more are contemplated (see COAL MINING). Electronic data processing equipment is now available for the control and operation of large scale locomotive systems both underground and on the surface, with all operations completely automatic including loading and discharging facilities. As regards other aspects of haulage, automatic control of complex conveyer networks with television scanning has become almost commonplace, while for some time now, automatic hoisting has been accepted as virtually a basic feature of the modern underground mine.

Mechanization at the face It is relatively easy to mechanize operations at the face where the material is comparatively soft, like coal or phosphate. Machines have been devised which cut out the roadways underground and other machines have been developed which automatically cut and load mineral on longwall faces. Hard rocks, however, such as metalliferous ores, are not amenable to cutting and it is difficult to mechanize the actual process of breaking down the ore from the parent mass underground because of its hardness and the irregular shape of many deposits. Thus most underground metalliferous mining methods involve dividing the ore body

into working sections (called *stopes*) and subsequently employing high EXPLOSIVES to blast the ore away from each working face exposed by the underground development tunnels.

In the blasting processes, holes about 1 to 2 inches (2.5 to 5 cm) in diameter are drilled 6 to 10 ft (2 to 3 m) into the face of the ore. Explosive charges are fed into these holes and then detonated, so bursting away the ore ready for loading into transport media for despatch to the surface. Although the amount of explosive varies widely with conditions, an average 10 ft (3 m) hole charged with 4 lb (2 kg) of explosive would yield about 3 tons of ore. Sometimes many explosive charges are detonated simultaneously or in rapid sequence and the use of a ton or more of explosive in one blast is not uncommon. Blasting is usually done between shifts so that men are not endangered and sufficient time is given for noxious fumes to be dispelled.

Scale of mining operations The approximate current annual world production of various minerals, ores and rocks given in millions of tons includes: metallic ores (2000), non-metallic ores (1400), road and building stones, sand and gravel (3500), and coal (3000).

Surface operations account for almost 70% of all mining production. When it is borne in mind that in some surface operations, in order to expose the deposit, the mass of overlying rock to be moved may be 10 to 20 times greater than the tonnage of the deposit itself, it is easy to appreciate that in world mining something like 50,000 million tons of material (including waste) are moved annually. The scale of each individual mining operation varies tremendously. Mines range in size from operations employing two or three workers and producing a few thousand tons of ore a year to giant South

African gold mines, each employing 15,000 men and winning many millions of tons of gold ore each year from depths up to 12,000 ft (3.7 km) below the surface. At such great depths the air passed through the workings must be cooled in giant refrigeration plants because of the high rock temperature.

The world's largest underground mine is the huge Kiruna iron ore mine in Swedish Lapland with an annual output of 15,000,000 tons of high grade magnetite. Top of the production league in surface mines is the Bingham Canyon copper mine in Utah, USA. Here almost 250,000 tons of waste rock are stripped each day and 90,000 tons of copper ore having a copper content of 0.7% are mined daily. Although this is called a surface mine the floor of the open pit is more than 2000 ft (0.6 km) below the surface.

The broad choice between open pit (also known as opencast)

mining or underground mining is decided after detailed consideration of many factors such as surface topography, geology of deposit and surrounding rock, size and possible value of the deposit, environmental restrictions, depth of the deposit and so on. Usually if a choice is possible, open pit mining is favoured as it is a cheaper system both as regards initial investment and subsequent working costs. A large modern underground mine may cost up to £50,000,000 to bring into production and a comparable open pit operation between a quarter and half of this amount.

Mining systems As previously stated, mining operations can be broadly classified under two main headings, that is, surface mining and underground mining, each capable of further subdivision. Surface mining includes such operations as open pit mines where the ore body extends downwards, and

Left and below left: two views of vast excavators used at opencast coal mines in Germany. The upper picture shows a bucket excavator stripping overburden from coal deposits at Helmstedt. The lower picture, taken at a lignite (brown coal) mine near Cologne, shows the size of the tracks on which these machines move. Note the man standing between the pair of tracks.

Below: in underground mining, ventilation and drainage are vital considerations, and the cost of providing them can be greater than that of extracting the ore. This cactus grab is sinking an airway for a mine at Broken Hill, New South Wales, Australia, which produces lead, silver and zinc.

Right: opencast mining is cheaper than underground mining. It involves removing the 'overburden' or waste material under which the ore is situated. In this opencast coal mine the overburden is removed by the huge walking dragline, loaded on to trucks and taken to the overburden tip. Once the coal is exposed, holes are drilled into the shelf and loaded with explosives which blast the ore onto the shelf below. Here it is either loaded on to trucks or on to a conveyer belt system and taken off for processing. Trucks are loaded by power shovels, which are nowadays electrically powered where the size of the deposit makes it economical.

strip mines where the deposit is of fairly limited vertical thickness, but extends for a considerable distance in the two horizontal directions. Coal seams near the surface are particularly suited to strip mining. Yet another form of surface mining is to be found when such minerals as granite and limestone are produced in QUARRIES.

Although alluvial mining of TIN has been practised for a century or more, the principle involved has been considerably developed in recent years. This new mining technique, known as *marine mining*, represents a significant extension to the surface mining scene. The technique involves the dredging from the sea bed of a multiplicity of valuable products ranging from diamonds to the more prosaic—but very important—sand and gravel deposits. These unconsolidated deposits are won by bucket wheel, grab or suction pump dredgers, and although

most commercial marine mining operations are confined to a maximum water depth of about 200 ft (60 m) or so, prototype air-lift pumps have been used to recover manganese nodules from the floor of the Pacific Ocean at a depth of 3000 ft (900 m). Some authorities believe that economic mining of the sea bed is possible down to 12,000 ft (3.6 km) depth and that the tonnage of valuable metals thus available exceeds total land reserves.

Another specific surface mining technique is *borehole mining*. This involves the sinking of boreholes from the surface. In the *Frasch process* for the mining of SULPHUR, boiling hot water is passed down pipes placed in a borehole. This water melts the sulphur, which is then pumped to the surface as a liquid. Another form of borehole mining involves passing a solvent down the borehole. This liquid dissolves the valuable deposit

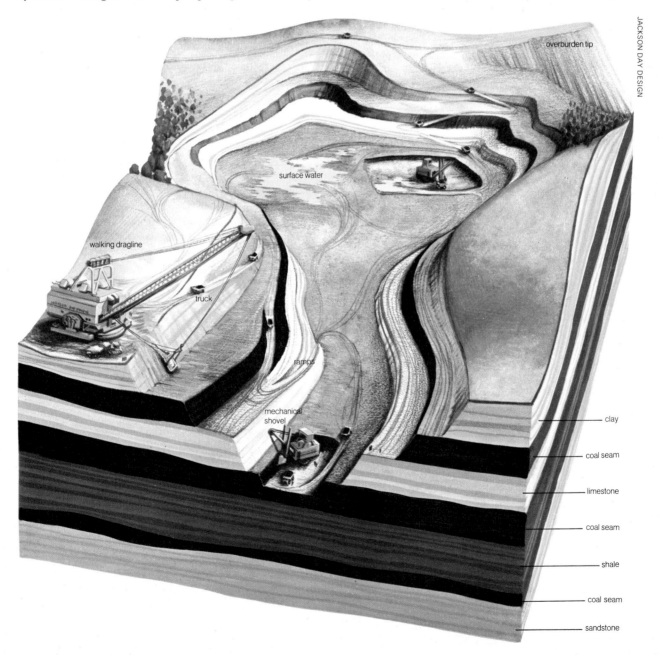

and the solution is then pumped back to the surface. This system is most commonly applied in SALT mining (using water as the solvent) but *solution mining* has, however, been used to selectively dissolve other minerals such as potash. On reaching the surface, the impregnated solution is treated and the valuable mineral regained.

In the mining of some relatively soft surface deposits such as CHINA CLAY, high pressure water jets (up to about 100 psi or 7 bar) are used to dislodge the valuable clay, which is then sluiced down to the treatment plant. This is known as *hydraulic mining*. This principle has also been employed to a limited extent in underground coal mines in Europe, in particular in the USSR.

There are various techniques for winning ores underground, depending on the extent, shape and geology of the deposit. Where large masses occur *caving* may be used; here tunnels are made in the mineral in such a way that, on blasting, it literally caves in from above, falling to the collecting level below. Alternatively, in *stoping*, the ore is systematically worked from various levels—a method suited to both mass and vein deposits. This also includes 'room and pillar' method, where various chambers are excavated by leaving pillars between to support the roof.

Special underground mining techniques
The underground gasification of poor quality coal seams is extensively used in certain coal mining areas, although limited trial installations in Britain and Western Europe have not proved too successful for various technical reasons. Broadly the system involves sinking shafts to the coal seam and then igniting the coal underground and piping the evolved gases to the surface. Such gases have a low calorific value—only about one fifth of that of natural gas—and thus it is not economical to pipe the gas a long distance on the surface to the point of utilization.

In metalliferous mining, a system which finds some application is the *leaching technique*. This technique incorporates principles of hydrometallurgy and essentially involves passing a weak acid over the broken ore underground. This acid selectively dissolves the metal from the broken rock and is then pumped back to the surface. In many respects in situ leaching is similar to the borehole mining previously described, the essential difference being that only a very small part of the deposit is dissolved—only the metal content, and this may be just a fraction of 1% of the mass of the ore deposit. The chief difficulty with in situ leaching is that almost invariably the ore mass must be broken up by normal mining operations; otherwise, the weak acid cannot attack sufficient ore. One possible economic method of breaking up sufficient ore is by the use of nuclear explosives underground. Although nuclear explosives have been detonated underground and the effects determined, such tests were in no way connected with mining operations and it is highly unlikely that nuclear mining will be permitted.

The very wide range of mining techniques briefly described will have shown that each mining prospect must be carefully assessed before any decision can be reached as to the method of mining to be employed. In some cases variations or combinations of standard techniques will provide the appropriate means of mining a deposit safely and economically.

Above: preparations for blasting at the Toquepala copper and molybdenum mine in southern Peru. The hole has been partly filled with ammonium nitrate and fuel oil, and 'stemming', a packing layer of sand, is being poured in on top.

Right: ore crushers treating iron ore at Mount Tom Price, Western Australia. The primary crusher is in the foreground.

COLORIFIC/PHOTO: MARY FISHER

COLORIFIC/PHOTO: JULIAN COWAN

MIRROR

All the objects around us reflect light. The surface of a mirror differs essentially from other surfaces only in being extremely smooth, so it does not jumble and diffuse the light rays that it reflects. Light rays diverging from an object will, after reflection by a mirror, continue to diverge, but from a new place. We judge an object to be at the place from which its light diverges. An observer will therefore judge light reflected from a mirror to come from a 'phantom' object—an *image*, which can be located behind or in front of a mirror surface. The study of image formation is part of the science of OPTICS.

The normal domestic mirror is flat and consists of a thin film of silver coated on the back of a sheet of glass. It forms images that are identical in appearance to their objects except that they are *laterally inverted*—for example, a left hand's mirror-image is a right hand. Other mirrors, such as car rear view mirrors, are convex, and form reduced laterally inverted images. Concave mirrors, such as shaving mirrors, form enlarged laterally inverted images of objects that are close to them. The distorting mirrors of a funfair are concave in parts, and convex in others, thus stretching and squeezing different parts of the image.

Images can be formed by multiple reflection: double reflection removes inversion. Using two ordinary mirrors, it is easy to make a mirror that forms a 'correct' or non-inverted image.

So-called one way mirrors consist of glass that has been coated with a layer of silver thinner than normal. This half-silvering reflects most of the light that falls on it (from either side), but permits some to pass through. On the observer's side of the mirror is a darkened room while on the other is a normally lit room. Most of the light from this side is reflected to form a bright image that masks the small amount passing through from the other side. Enough light passes through the mirror from the normally lit room to give the observer a clear view of it.

Mirror production Metals have always been favoured for mirrors because they are highly reflective, able to be cast and polished to a high degree of smoothness, and hard wearing. Bronze hand mirrors, often highly ornate, were made by the Egyptians, Etruscans, Greeks and Romans in the centuries before Christ. Luxury mirrors were made of silver.

The Roman writer Pliny reports the existence of mirrors made of glass coated with tin or silver, but this principle was not in common use until the Middle Ages. It was first used on a large scale by Venetian craftsmen in the 16th century. They would lay a large sheet of tinfoil flat and coat it with mercury (which is liquid at normal temperatures), squeezing out excess mercury by laying a sheet of paper on top of this. Then a sheet of glass was gently laid on the paper, and the paper withdrawn. An *amalgam*, a chemical combination of tin and mercury, would coat the lower surface of the glass. It only remained to mount the whole on a protective backing.

This craft was supplanted in the 19th century by a chemical process invented by Justus von Liebig (1803–1873), who discovered how to deposit silver on to glass from a solution. This process is used today to make mirrors for everyday purposes. To prevent the delicate silver layer from being scratched, a coating of copper sulphate and other chemicals is added,

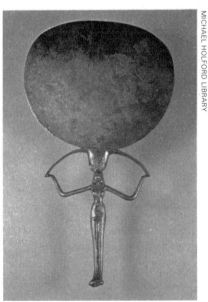

Left: a searchlight mirror provides amusement, but illustrates the image-forming properties of a concave surface. Shaving mirrors which magnify work on the same principle.

Above: this bronze Egyptian mirror once had a highly polished surface and would have given a good reflection, but has long since corroded.

finished with a layer of paint. One way mirrors dispense with these, and use transparent lacquer instead.

The glass of an ordinary mirror serves the purpose of providing a very flat surface, and of protecting the reflective silvering. It has the disadvantage of absorbing some of the light that passes through it, giving rise to multiple reflection, which in turn creates multiple images. These are too faint to be troublesome in everyday use, but in scientific work, mirrors are frequently front-silvered to avoid multiple images.

The concave mirror used in a modern reflecting ASTRONOMICAL TELESCOPE, for example, normally consists of an aluminium or chromium-plus-aluminium film coated on to the accurately shaped glass or ceramic surface. The coating is formed by *vacuum deposition*: a small piece of the desired metal is placed on a heating coil in a vacuum chamber. It vaporizes, and the vapour deposits on the uncoated glass, which is also placed in the vacuum chamber. The resulting film is only a few millionths of an inch thick, and can easily be removed chemically when necessary. It can then be renewed without disturbing the accurately ground glass surface. It is common to re-aluminize telescope and similar optics every couple of years or so, when the surface becomes less reflective, and large telescopes have their own built-in aluminizing plant, close by the observing floor.

Below: whether or not a surface behaves as a mirror depends on its roughness compared with the wavelength of light being used. At left is a surface which has irregularities of the same order of size as the light being used. The light is scattered in all directions— known as diffuse reflection—as from a piece of paper. But the smoother surface at right acts as a mirror—specular reflection.

Above: most mirrors for scientific and technical uses are aluminized on the front surface. This large vacuum coating device is shown after being used to coat a reflector for use in a flight simulator.

Left: if a mirror turns through a given angle, its image turns through twice that angle—the principle of this infra-red line scanning device for making heat images. Mirrors reflect all wavelengths equally.

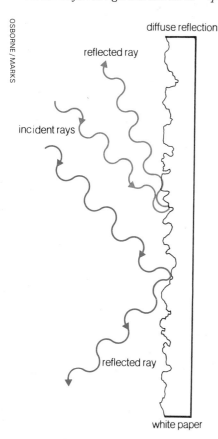

diffuse reflection

reflected ray

incident rays

reflected ray

white paper

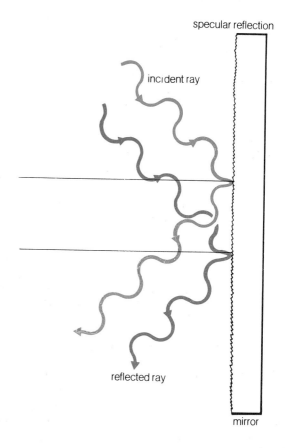

specular reflection

incident ray

reflected ray

mirror

MISSILE

A guided missile is an unmanned self-propelled airborne vehicle or spacecraft which carries a destructive load; it may be remotely guided or direct itself to a preselected target. Whatever its specific purpose might be, a missile consists of an airframe, with or without wings and fins, housing a motor, control system, guidance system and warhead.

Airframe and motor

The configuration and size of a missile are governed by its range and the type of motor used to propel it. Largest of all are *intercontinental ballistic missiles* (ICBMs), with a range of at least 8000 km (5000 miles), requiring multi-stage ROCKET motors which take them to a height of up to 1600 km (1000 miles). The cylindrical propellant tanks for liquid-propellant motors, or cylindrical casings of solid-propellant motors, often form the outer skin of the missile, the individual stages of which are jettisoned after burnout, leaving the warhead to complete the trajectory to impact alone. No wings or fins are fitted, as most of the missile's flight is outside the Earth's atmosphere, where aerodynamic surfaces would be ineffective. Materials used for the rocket casings include maraging steel (alloy steel subjected to a heat treatment to impart toughness) high strength aluminium alloy and glassfibre.

Air-breathing or *cruise* missiles, designed to travel within the atmosphere, utilize ramjet or turbojet engines (see JET ENGINES). They need air intakes for these engines, and wings or fins to sustain them in flight. Consequently, their design often resembles that of a piloted AIRCRAFT. The earliest and best known example was the World War 2 V-1 flying BOMB.

Most other categories of missile have a cylindrical body fitted with cruciform wings and either cruciform tail-fins or nose-mounted foreplanes. Depending on the required maximum speed, the wings may be rectangular, sweptback or delta, sometimes with a *chord* (the line joining the centres of curvature of the leading and trailing edges of an aerofoil section), many times their span. When such missiles are launched from a tube, or from inside the bomb-bay of an aircraft, it is normal for the wings to be hinged, so that they fold around the body, and to be spring-loaded so that they extend after launch.

Solid-propellant booster rockets are often attached to the body of missiles, particularly those with ramjet or turbojet engines, to give a high initial launch speed. The boosters jettison after burnout.

Control system

Missiles which operate within the Earth's atmosphere are able to utilize aerodynamic control surfaces (see AEROFOIL) moved by electrical, hydraulic or pneumatic actuators. Either the cruciform wings or the tail surfaces may be pivoted for this purpose. Less frequently, the use of wing-mounted ailerons or elevons, or pivoted vertical and horizontal tail surfaces, or a combination of both, provides an even closer similarity to the control surfaces of a piloted aircraft.

An alternative to aerodynamic control is some form of *vectored thrust*, which is effective in both atmosphere and space. In large missiles, such as ICBMs, it is usual to gimbal the nozzles of the rocket motors, thus steering the missiles by changing the direction of thrust. A similar deflection of thrust can be achieved by liquid injection on one inner wall of the nozzle, or by blanking off part of the nozzle. This last technique, employing pivoted 'semaphores', is particularly suitable for close-range air-launched anti-aircraft missiles, which must have high manoeuvrability to match that of the target.

Right: firing a McDonnell Douglas XM-47 Dragon anti-tank missile. The Dragon and its launcher together weigh only 27 pounds (12.3 kg) and so are easily carried by one man. It is directed to the target by a wire guidance ('command-to-line-of-sight') system.

Below: a BAC Rapier surface-to-air missile launcher. The Rapier is designed for use against low-flying aircraft and may be either optically aimed or guided by a radar tracking system.

Above: an F-101B fighter firing a Genie air-to-air missile. The Genie was 9.5 ft (2.9 m) long, and had a solid fuel rocket motor which gave it a range of up to 6 miles (9.7 km).

Left: a Minuteman ICBM being launched from its underground silo. The smoke ring is formed by exhaust from the rocket motor passing up between the missile and the silo wall after ignition.

Guidance system The most important component of a missile is the system which ensures that it hits the correct target. Some guidance systems are self-contained within the missile; these often have the advantage of being less susceptible to enemy electronic countermeasures (ECM) or JAMMING. Others involve continuous monitoring of the missile's position, and course corrections, during flight.

One of the simplest forms of guidance for short-range missiles is wire guidance. As the missile travels towards its target, it trails one or two fine wires which unwind from bobbins and continue to link it with the operator's controls. He can steer it into the target, using a thumbstick or miniature aircraft-type joystick to generate electrical signals which are transmitted over the wires to the missile's control system. The weight of the wires limits range to about two miles, and both target and missile must be visible to the operator. Tracking flares attached to the missile help him follow its path as distance from the launcher increases, especially in poor light or rough country.

At a small cost in complexity, it is possible to dispense with the wires by transmitting signals by radio between the operator and the missile (*radio command guidance*). This increases the danger of enemy ECM interference, requiring use of a range of signal frequencies, one of which must be selected and fed into the missile electronics before launch, so that it will ignore signals on all other frequencies. Devices to afford further protection (ECCM: electronic counter-countermeasures) can also be built into the missile.

If the missile is to be fired against a target beyond visual range, a cathode ray viewer rather like a TV screen is used. The precise position of the target, if fixed and known, can be set up on the screen. The missile can then be tracked by RADAR in flight, and its 'blip' steered into the target. Greater accuracy can be achieved by fitting a small TV camera into the nose of the missile. Then, as it approaches the target, the controller receives a TV picture of the target area and can steer the missile

SPECTRUM

JOHN TAYLOR

Above: an Honest John tactical surface-to-surface missile used for battlefield support as a powerful alternative to heavy artillery. It is almost 25 ft (7.6 m) long, with a range of 23 miles (37 km).

Right: a Poseidon submarine-launched ballistic missile, a two stage solid fuel rocket powered missile carrying a nuclear warhead. It has a range of about 3000 miles (4828 km).

to a precisely-chosen pinpoint. Such techniques have enabled controllers in aircraft to hit a particular bridge support or part of a ship beyond visual range.

An advantage of such a system is that the launch aircraft can turn back towards its base once the missile has been launched, without any loss of control over the flight path. This permits launch and control over 'stand-off' ranges, beyond the reach of the target's close defences.

Another TV guidance technique entails 'locking' the camera on to the target before launching the missile, which will then home automatically on where the camera is aimed, by means of onboard electronics.

Radar tracking is used widely for surface-launched anti-aircraft missiles, advantages being that it can, if required, eliminate the need for manual steering and is fully effective in bad weather or at night. The automatic system requires two radars, to track the target and missile respectively. Radar information is fed into a computer, which causes signals to be transmitted to the missile so that it will intercept the target. This is called *radar command guidance*.

Only one radar is needed for *beam-riding guidance*. After the radar has been locked on to the target, a missile is launched and guided into the radar beam. It locks on to the beam and flies along it to the target. *Semi-active homing* is somewhat similar. This involves 'illuminating' the target with a radar, causing radar signals to be reflected back from it. The missile then homes on to the source of the reflected signals. *Active homing* differs in that the missile both transmits and receives the signals, making it independent of radar transmitters on the ground or in a launch aircraft.

Active homing missiles tend to be comparatively large and complex. By comparison, those which employ passive homing are among the simplest of all, requiring no transmitters of any kind although they are self-contained. Typical are missiles fitted with an infra-red heat-seeking head. This locates any source

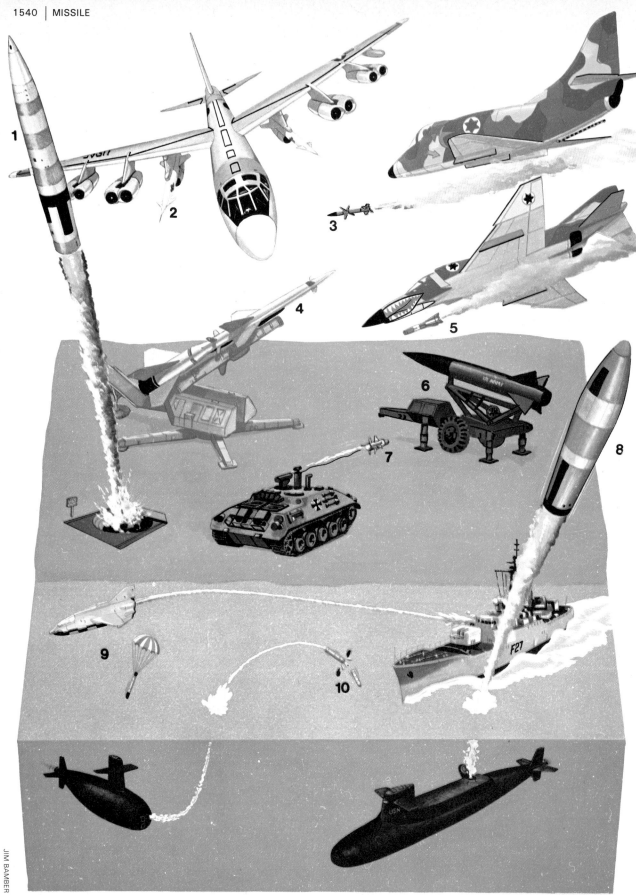

Left: ten types of missile currently in service.
1 Minuteman (USA), three-stage solid-fuelled intercontinental ballistic missile, thermonuclear MIRV (multiple independently-targetable re-entry vehicles) warhead.
2 Hound Dog (USA), air-to-surface thermonuclear missile, turbojet-powered, inertial guidance and star-tracking systems.
3 Shrike (USA), supersonic air-to-surface anti-radar missile, solid-propellant rocket, high-explosive warhead, homes on enemy radars.
4 SAM-2 (USSR), surface-to-air missile. Two-stage rocket (solid and liquid), radio-guided and detonated (also has conventional fuzes).
5 Maverick (USA), tactical air-to-surface missile, solid-propellant rocket. Self-homing TV system with camera in nose locks on to target automatically once aimed, leaving pilot free to turn away.
6 Lance (USA), surface-to-surface artillery missile, liquid-propellant rocket powered, nuclear or high-explosive warhead.
7 HOT (France & Germany), anti-tank missile, wire-guided, two-stage solid-propellant rocket motor.
8 Poseidon (USA), underwater-to-surface ballistic missile, solid-propellant rocket, thermonuclear MIRV warhead.
9 Ikara (Australia), long-range anti-submarine missile, solid-propellant rocket powered, carries torpedo to target and drops it by parachute (transparent 'cockpit canopy' covers instruments only).
10 Subroc (USA), underwater-to-underwater missile, solid-propellant rockets, inertial guidance system. Fired from submarine, surfaces, travels to target, drops nuclear depth bomb.

of heat emission, such as the exhaust of an aircraft jet engine, and homes on to it. Another homing technique uses LASER designators to achieve high effectiveness even in a rapidly changing combat environment. A controller on the ground, or in an aircraft, locates a target and directs a laser beam on to it. The missile then picks up the reflected laser beam and homes on to the source of the reflections.

Most advanced system of all is inertial guidance, being self-contained in the missile, unjammable and extremely accurate. It uses ACCELEROMETERS and GYROSCOPES to measure every slight change of direction of the missile during flight. If any change would take it off its predetermined course to the target, the guidance system moves the controls to put it right (see INERTIAL NAVIGATION).

Warhead Missiles can carry almost any kind of military warhead, including those associated with chemical or biological warfare. Anti-tank wire-guided missiles, for example, can be fitted with interchangeable ARMOUR PIERCING types able to penetrate 600 mm (24 inches) of steel, high-explosive or anti-personnel fragmentation types. The largest Soviet ICBMs can carry a 25-megaton thermonuclear warhead, a cluster of individually-targeted thermonuclear warheads able to man-œuvre to elude the defences, or a 'space bomb' that can be put into orbit and directed down on to its target at will. Small nuclear warheads can be fitted to almost any class of missile. High-explosive types are normally fitted with both contact and proximity fuzes.

The effectiveness of ICBMs has been increased by the development of *multiple re-entry vehicles* (MRVs) and *multiple independently targetable re-entry vehicles* (MIRVs). MRVs have several small warheads carried by one missile, which are released in controlled sequence as the missile passes over the target (rather like an aircraft dropping bombs), thus spreading the damage over a wider area. MIRVs take this idea a stage further by ejecting the warheads from the 'bus' (main missile) at predetermined times, with different directions and velocities, so that one ICBM can attack several separate targets.

Top: a Regulus surface-to-surface missile which was launched from a ship or from the deck of a surfaced submarine. The Regulus was capable of delivering a nuclear warhead, and was a predecessor of the Polaris, which was first launched in 1958 and entered service with the US Navy in 1961.

Above: a selection of aircraft weapons including cannon, bombs, and missiles. Air-to-air missiles usually have high-explosive warheads, and air-to-surface missiles are either high-explosive or nuclear.

MIXER, food

Food mixing processes include stirring, beating, whisking, kneading, chopping and blending, and each of these actions can be carried out with electric food mixers. The various types of mixers are often designed with their performance emphasized towards one or other of these operations.

One of the earliest electric mixers was the 'Universal Electric Mixer Beater' which was first produced about 1918 and consisted of the well established kitchen whisk coupled to an electric motor. Another early mixer was the 'Peerless' industrial machine built in 1927, but it was not until after World War 2 that domestic food mixers started to become popular.

Large mixers Large domestic mixers can be either the *orbiting action* or the *revolving bowl* type. Both use a *series wound* ELECTRIC MOTOR designed to give the correct speed-torque characteristics for the mixer. With this type of motor a fixed ratio reduction gearbox is used and the speed of the mixer is controlled by means of a GOVERNOR attached to the end of the motor shaft. Under the action of centrifugal force the governor weights fly outwards. The centre of the governor arm moves out and bears on a pair of spring contacts which interrupt the electricity supply to the motor when the selected speed is exceeded. These contacts may control the motor directly or they may be connected to a SEMICONDUCTOR device which switches the main power to the motor. In the latter arrangement, the contacts only handle very light currents and their life is considerably extended. By moving the contacts away from or towards the governor, control of the speed can be obtained by a hand operated mechanism. CAPACITORS are connected across the contacts and across the supply connections

BAKER PERKINS

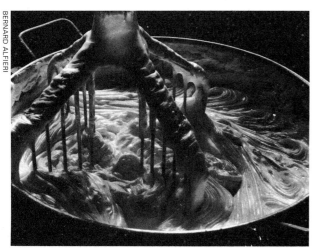

BERNARD ALFIERI

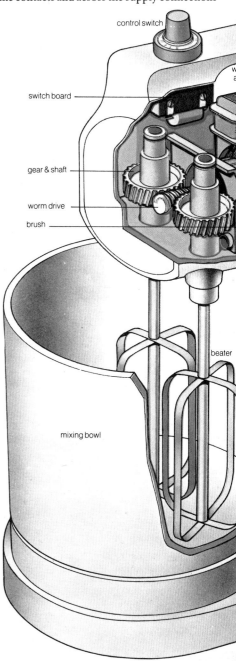

JOHN BISHOP

control switch

switch board

gear & shaft

worm drive

brush

beater

mixing bowl

Below left: a continuous automatic mixing machine. The material to be mixed is passed to the mixing chamber (centre left) by a pump.

Bottom left: mixing machines are used in many industries apart from the food industry. This picture shows soap being mixed.

Below: a small domestic food mixer has a pair of interpenetrating beaters which are driven in opposite directions by a worm gear meshing with gear wheels fixed to the top of each shaft. The worm gear is directly attached to the motor shaft, and the speed of the motor can be varied by a switch which connects different field coil windings to the power supply. A fan fixed to the drive shaft behind the motor cools the field windings during operation.

Below right: the 'Universal Electric Mixer Beater', an early type.

to reduce the radio interference which would otherwise be caused by interruption of the mains supply.

The drive from the motor is taken to a gearbox by means of a toothed drive to avoid slip and to provide some speed reduction. In a typical design the motor is also brought to an outlet on the machine where a mechanical connection can be made to a liquidizer goblet or other attachment. The gearbox consists of a series of connecting *spur* GEARS which reduce the speed from the motor to a speed suitable for carrying out the various operations of the mixer. The reduction gearbox has additional outlets which provide power take off points to additional attachments. A horizontal shaft is driven from the main vertical drive by a pair of *bevel gears* and, in orbiting action machines, this drives a hub situated above the mixing bowl into which the beater, whisk or kneader is inserted. The socket for the mixing

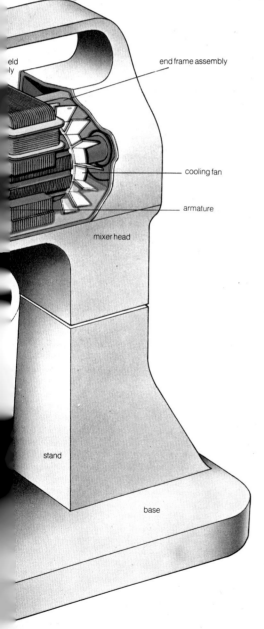

end frame assembly

cooling fan

armature

mixer head

stand

base

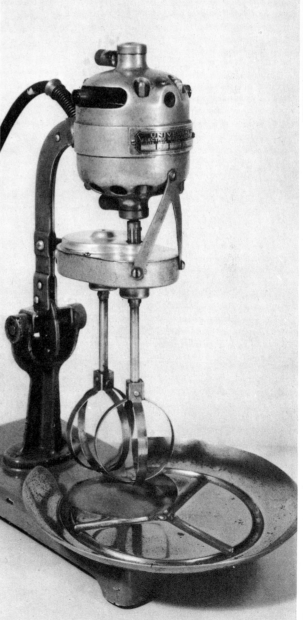

THE SCIENCE MUSEUM / KENWOOD

tool is itself connected to a further gear, a *planet gear*, which meshes with a fixed *ring gear* mounted on the lower side of the hub gearbox. Rotation of the hub causes the planet gear to rotate about its own centre as its teeth engage the ring gear so that the mixing tool rotates about its own axis and also 'orbits' around the centre of the bowl. Each point of the tool has an *epicyclic* motion and all parts of the mixture are stirred. In revolving bowl machines, the mixing tool rotates on a fixed axis and the bowl itself rotates.

Industrial food mixers emphasize the kneading, beating and stirring actions. The mixer consists of an *induction motor* driving, by means of a change speed gearbox, a planetary gear combination inside a hub into which one or more beaters, dough hooks or wire whisks can be inserted. These tools are arranged to revolve on their own axes and also in a circle around the centre of the bowl. On the very largest of mixers the epicyclic action can become cumbersome, and in this case the beaters revolve on a fixed axis and the bowl itself is rotated with a separate drive.

Small mixers

Small domestic mixers use a different principle. Their design emphasizes the whisking and beating actions and also allows lighter hand held appliances to be made. The essential components are a pair of whisks or beaters mounted vertically and spaced a short distance apart so that their blades interpenetrate each other. The beater shafts are driven in opposite directions by a pair of *helical gears* which lie on opposite sides of a *worm gear*. The worm gear is mounted directly on the motor shaft. The contra-rotating motion draws material through the beaters mixing it thoroughly in the process. Circulation of material in stand mounted mixers is achieved by turning the bowl which is mounted on a plate supported by a low friction BEARING. The beaters are held to one side of the bowl and the viscous drag of the material being mixed turns the bowl automatically.

These mixers are usually fitted with *universal* motors, that is, electric motors which can be operated from a direct current source or a single phase alternating current supply. In motors of this type the armature speed is inversely proportional to the magnetic field and this allows the speed of the mixer to be varied by varying the number of turns on the field winding. Generally a number of coils are wound on top of each other and a simple three position switch selects the coil required for the appropriate speed. An alternative method of controlling the speed is to use a THYRISTOR regulator. Such a control permits infinitely variable speed adjustment and automatically maintains the speed irrespective of the output torque.

Liquidizers

Another type of domestic mixer is the liquidizer or blender. These machines combine the actions of chopping and stirring, often by macerating solids in a liquid suspension. Blenders consist of two main parts, a *goblet* and a *power unit*. The goblet contains a number of small sharpened blades on a shaft which passes through a liquid tight bearing in the base. The shaft is connected to the power unit by means of a plastic or rubber coupling designed to allow for any misalignment. The power unit consists of a series wound universal electric motor fitted inside a casing to which it is attached with rubber mountings. The blender or liquidizer blades are driven at high speed, usually about 12,000 rpm, and the rotating blades form a vortex or whirlpool in the liquid so that the solid particles are drawn down on to the cutting blades. Vertical ribs moulded inside the goblet control the vortex formation and assist vertical circulation of the particles. A series wound motor is used because it can be designed to give peak efficiency at high speed. Liquidizers have not always been fitted with speed controls, but some of the more recent models fit a thyristor control similar to that used on a hand-held mixer.

Above: an industrial tilting bowl mixing machine for mixing biscuit dough. The bowl has a capacity of 850 kg (1870 lb) and the mixing process is controlled automatically.

Right: an industrial mixing machine in which the ingredients are automatically weighed and fed to the mixing bowl. The two large weigher dials can be seen above the control panel.

MIXING, sound

Sound mixing techniques have evolved out of a need in certain branches of the entertainments industry to have independent control over the sound relationships of simultaneously performing artists when using broadcasting, recording or public address (PA) systems. For example, when recording an orchestra it is often necessary to have separate control over the sound balance, that is the loudness and tonal quality, of the various sections of musical instruments.

To achieve this independence or 'separation', each sound component must be picked up by a separate MICROPHONE or TRANSDUCER, for example a guitar or piano PICK-UP. The electrical signals from each microphone (or from previously recorded tapes) are fed to the input channels of a *sound mixer*. The sound, or *audio*, mixer, as its name implies, mixes and modifies the various signals to give a desired output signal which can then be broadcast or recorded. Sound mixers vary in size and complexity from simple devices consisting of two or three input channels (one input socket and a volume or *level* control making up each channel) to be found in small 'on stage' set ups, to the large and complex mixing consoles or 'desks' with hundreds of switches and slider level controls, called *faders*, used in modern recording studios.

Mixing desks
A typical recording studio mixing desk would have perhaps 20 to 30 identical input channels and from 2 to 24 *output mixing groups*, plus a small *monitor mixer* and control panel. The output from each output mixing group is passed to one track of a multi-track TAPE RECORDER.

The input channels each have a microphone AMPLIFIER for boosting the low level microphone signals to a level suitable for feeding to the next part of the channel, called the *equalizer*. This is a unit similar to the tone recording device used in domestic HI-FI equipment, but having in addition to the normal bass (low frequency) and treble (high frequency) boost and cut controls, a number of middle frequency or *presence* controls. The equalizer is a very important part of any mixing unit as it enables the balance engineer to modify the tonal quality or timbre of an instrumental or vocal sound. This could be done to correct deficiencies in a microphone or the acoustics of a room, or to enhance the tonal character of a performance.

The modified signals from the equalizer are next passed into the channel distribution or *routing unit*. This permits the signal passing through the channel to be sent to any of the various output mixing groups of the mixer, either before or after passing through the channel main fader, which determines how much of the signal leaving the channel will be sent to the selected output mixing group. It is in these mixing groups that the signals from the various channels are electronically mixed together and amplified to a suitable level for sending on outgoing lines to the tape machine. Each group has a level control to enable overall changes to be made in the level of the outgoing mixed signals.

In addition to the main mixing system, mixing desks often have completely separate multi-channel systems each having a separate fader for each channel and its own master level control. Such auxiliary mixing systems are used for mixing together signals to be sent to *echo plates* or other special effects devices. The returning signals from these devices are fed back into spare input channels on the main mixer, and this allows echo or special effects to be added independently of any of the numerous signals entering the mixer. Auxiliary mixing systems are also used for returning the incoming signals to the artists.

Below: the mixing desk of a modern recording studio. The desk has 16 output mixing groups, each of which is passed directly or indirectly to one track of a 16 track tape machine.

POLYDOR/PHOTO: MIKE ST MAUR SHEIL

This *foldback* mix is sent to headphones or loudspeakers in the studio to allow the artists to hear clearly the sounds as picked up by the microphones.

The final stage of the mixer is the monitor system which enables the balance engineer to construct a mix of the signals leaving the mixing desk or the signals already recorded on tape for feeding to control room monitor loudspeakers. The monitor mixer is independent of the main mixing system and only controls the way in which the signals are heard by the engineer. Changes made to a monitor mix do not affect the signals being recorded on the tape.

Recording Modern recordings are usually made by recording the separate component sounds on different tracks of a multi-track tape recorder. Up to 24 tracks can be simultaneously recorded on 2 inch (5.1 cm) wide tape. When a mixing desk is used with this type of machine only one or two microphone

signals are mixed into each output group and thereby on to each track of the tape. This allows the sounds contained on each track to be treated independently at a later stage during or after completion of the recording. Finally the multi-track tape is replayed into the mixing desk, the output from each track being fed to separate input channels of the mixer. The signals are remixed down to one or two output groups and recorded on to standard $\frac{1}{4}$ inch (0.63 cm) tape from which a record may be cut (see STEREO RECORDING).

This type of recording dominates the modern recording industry as it allows for greater flexibility than direct recording. Each component part can be recorded separately and even at different times, and the remixing process can be carried out at the convenience of the studio. Once a good performance has been captured on the multi-track tape the remixing can be carried out as often as is necessary to achieve the desired result.

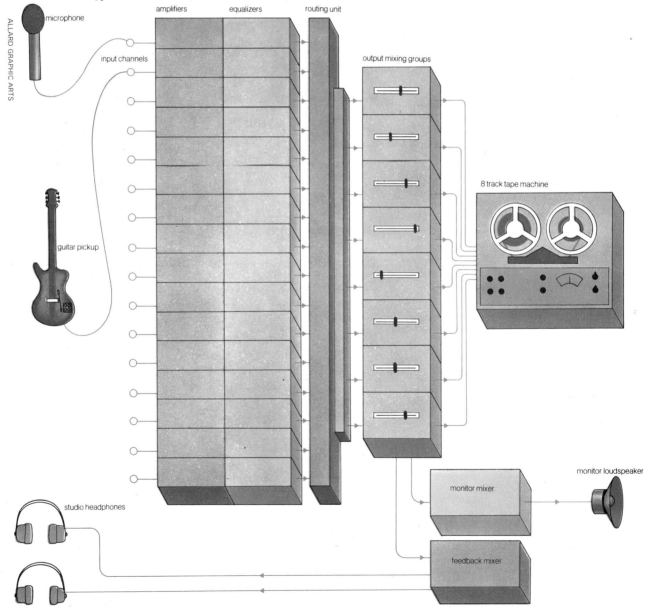

ALLARD GRAPHIC ARTS

MIXTURE

A mixture is a combination of chemical ELEMENTS or COMPOUNDS which can be separated by physical or mechanical methods. In other words the components of a mixture are not bound together chemically. Where the molecules of one component are uniformly dispersed throughout the other component (usually a liquid), the mixture is called a *solution*.

Air is a mixture of oxygen, nitrogen, inert gases (all elements) and carbon dioxide (a compound). It can be separated into its various components by freezing out the carbon dioxide, and then liquefying and distilling (see DISTILLATION) the remaining gases. Seawater is a solution in water of various SALTS, the chief of which is sodium chloride. It can be separated by distilling off the water as in some DESALINATION processes and then separating the remaining salts from one another by techniques such as *fractional crystallization*, which makes use of the ability of some salts to crystallize out of solution before others. ALLOYS are examples of solid solutions; one or more metals being dissolved (to some extent) in another metal.

Separation of mixtures

Processes for separating mixtures into their components are important in almost every branch of industry. When crude ores have been dug from the ground they must be treated, or *dressed*, to concentrate the ore before the metals are extracted. Ore dressing relies on the physical differences between the valuable ore and the worthless material, or *gangue*, and the chief methods are gravity, flotation, magnetic and electrostatic concentration. Sometimes differences in colour or lustre are used to separate particularly rich pieces of ore by picking them off a moving conveyer belt by hand.

Gravity separation relies on differences in density between the various components of the ore. A good example of this method is gold *panning* where the crushed ore is agitated in a shallow pan containing water and the particles of gold, being much denser than the remainder of the ore, eventually settle to the bottom of the pan. Another gravity method makes use of a table-like surface inclined a few degrees to the horizontal and having shallow corrugations running along its length at right angles to the direction of inclination. A reciprocating mechanism vibrates the table in a direction parallel to its corrugations, and crushed ore and water are fed to an upper corner. Heavy ores travel along the table to its far end, while the lighter components are washed over the lower edge.

Magnetic methods of separation are commonly used to separate ores which contain iron. In one such method, two conveyer belts, situated one above the other, cross at right angles in a magnetic field. The crushed ore travels along the lower conveyer belt and the particles of iron-containing ore are attracted to the upper belt as the ore passes through the magnetic field. The non-magnetic components of the ore remain on the lower belt. Electrostatic separation is used for concentrating some non-metallic ores. The principle is similar to that of magnetic separation, but an electrostatic field is used instead of a magnetic field.

Separation by flotation relies on differences in the surface properties of the various components of the ore. When mixed with water some ores are more easily wetted than others. Particles of an ore which resists wetting will attach themselves to air bubbles and float to the surface of the mixture where they can be removed as a froth. Although some minerals, such as talc, are naturally water repellent, it is usually necessary to add a chemical to the flotation bath to impart water repellent properties to the ore before separation by flotation is possible. Frothing is induced by adding a chemical frothing agent to the flotation bath.

Most of the chemical, pharmaceutical and food industries make extensive use of separation techniques such as distillation (see OIL REFINING), FILTRATION and solvent extraction.

Below: the flotation method is used to separate lead sulphide ore (galena) from zinc sulphide ore (sphalerite).

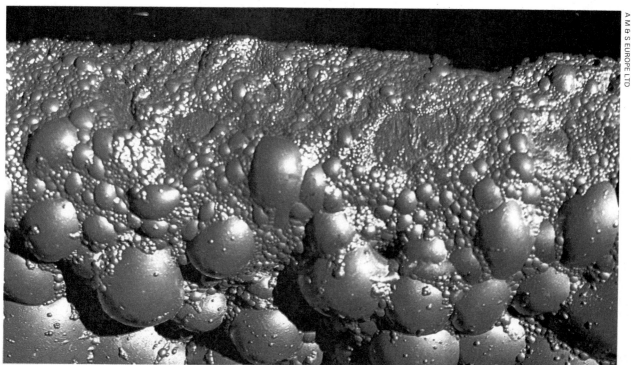

MODEL, remote controlled

There are two main types of remote control for models: cable control, in which the control signals are passed to the model along a cable, and RADIO control where the signals are transmitted to the model by radio.

The cable controlled models are not common because they are limited in range (to the length of the cable) and because of the increased power needed by the model to drag the cable with it.

Models controlled by radio transmission, however, have very long operating ranges using modern equipment, and can also have very precise and complex control systems. The most common radio controlled models are boats, cars and aircraft, of which aircraft are perhaps the most complex because they operate in three dimensions. The description that follows is of model aircraft, but the basic principles apply to all models.

Single channel control   There are two types of radio control (RC) equipment: single channel (SC) and multi-channel. As its name suggests, SC controls only one function of the model, generally the steering. Multi-channel systems can, in a model aircraft, control the rudder, elevator, ailerons, under-

Below: the single channel (S/C) remote controlled model is the simplest type available, as it permits the control of one function only—usually the steering (rudder). The transmitted signal is amplified by the receiver which controls the actuator—this moves the rudder. To the right is the basic scheme for a multi-channel remote control system. Signals for controlling the various functions are combined (coded) into one signal for transmission and separated by the decoder in the model to actuate servomechanisms.

carriage, engine speed and brakes. In most countries there are regulations governing the use of radio for remote controlled models. In the UK the allocated frequencies are between 26.96 and 27.28 megahertz (MHz).

The simplest SC equipment consists of a transmitter, a receiver, a RELAY, and an electromechanical device to operate the function called an *actuator* or *escapement*. When the button or keying switch on the transmitter is pressed, a constant-frequency signal is sent to the model and amplified by the receiver. This amplified signal is used to operate the relay, which in turn operates the actuator.

The actuator is connected to the rudder of the model by a crank. When the actuator SOLENOID operates, a pre-tensioned rubber loop rotates a pawl as the escapement arm moves toward the solenoid core. The pawl only moves 90° before striking the other lug of the escapement arm. Thus the actuator shaft rotates 90° and moves the rudder.

When the transmitter button is released, the actuator solenoid is de-energized and the pawl rotates a further 90° to a neutral position. The next transmitter operation will give the opposite control direction as the crank has now rotated 270° from its original neutral position. Thus sequential operation (left-neutral-right-neutral-left and so on) is obtained.

More powerful receivers with higher output levels dispense with the need for relays, but it was not until the introduction of multi-channel operation that really comprehensive systems became possible.

Multi-channel control   The first multi channel equipment used a *tone transmitter*, which could send up to 12 different tones. Each tone would cause one of 12 reeds in the

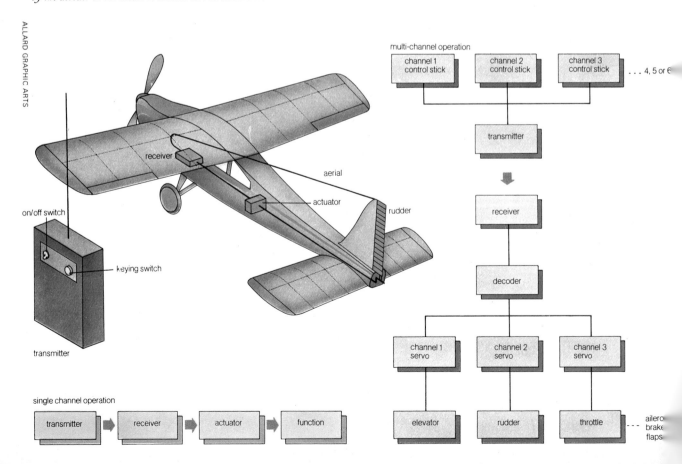

ALLARD GRAPHIC ARTS

receiver to vibrate and close a contact, causing a SERVO-MECHANISM (servo) to operate the desired function. This early equipment was bulky, heavy and not very reliable.

Modern multi-channel equipment uses *digital pulsing systems* to obtain proportional control, an important advantage over SC systems which can move a function fully left or right but not to an intermediate position. This makes it possible to use a lever on the transmitter (like the control column of a real aircraft) which if moved any amount causes a proportional movement of the model function.

The transmitter generates a series of pulses all the time it is on. A group of pulses or *frame* contains one more pulse than the number of channels (controllable functions on the model). This is because the receiver reads the 'spaces' as pulses. About 50 to 80 frames per second are sent by the transmitter to the receiver, which amplifies the signal and sends it to a decoder.

The decoder reads the spaces and sends them to the appropriate servo, that is space one to servo one, space two to servo two, and so on. The spaces are, of course equivalent to pulses relative to the transmitter pulses and are of approximately 1.5 milliseconds duration. Thus the decoder is sending a series of pulses of the same duration to each servo. The decoder recognizes the beginning and end of a frame because of the longer pause between each frame (about 5 milliseconds).

When the servo receives its pulse, it uses the leading edge of the pulse to generate another pulse of the same length, but opposite polarity. These two pulses are fed to the servo motor that is mechanically linked to the model function to be controlled. Since the pulses are equal but opposite, they cancel out and the motor does not operate.

When the control lever on the transmitter is moved it causes the appropriate space to change in duration. Thus if the rudder control lever is moved to the left the pulse lengthens, if it is moved to the right the pulse shortens. Now when this pulse arrives at the servo it no longer matches the one generated by the servo circuitry, and the two no longer cancel out so the motor turns and operates the rudder.

As soon as the motor starts to turn it operates a feedback POTENTIOMETER which alters the servo pulse. Thus if the transmitted signal has been increased the servo signal will increase until it is the same length as the transmitted one. At this point the two signals cancel out and the motor will stop. Since the transmitted pulse length is proportional to the amount the transmitter lever is moved, the amount the servo moves is also proportional to this movement. When the lever is returned to neutral the servo will follow. Any or all levers on the transmitter can be moved at any time, so a high degree of skill is called for when controlling a model.

Model aircraft and their control equipment are now very complex and expensive. The latest development is the radio controlled helicopter which, until Dieter Schluter of Germany developed one in 1972, had defeated the efforts of many modellers. Now a kit, together with control equipment, can be bought for about £400 ($925). One model helicopter (a model Bell 212) was flown across the English Channel on 17 July 1974, controlled by its owner, Dieter Ziegler of Munich, who flew 100 feet (30 m) from the model in a Bell Jet Ranger helicopter.

MODULATION (see amplitude, frequency, pulse code)

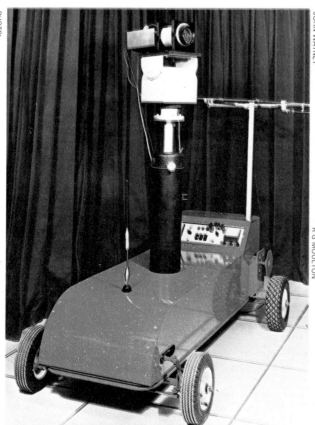

Far left: a model built to test the control system for a lunar rover vehicle which is remotely controlled with the aid of a television system.

Left: using a transmitter unit to test a model's functions.

Below: Dieter Ziegler prior to his flight from Ashford, Kent, to Boulogne, France. Flying at 500 ft (152 m) the flight took 67 minutes and the model used 1.5 litres (2.6 pints) of fuel.

MOLECULE

A molecule consists of two or more ATOMS, which may be the same as each other or different, bound together by chemical BONDS. A molecule is the basic unit of a chemical COMPOUND.

Many of the gaseous ELEMENTS are composed of molecules rather than atoms. The OXYGEN in the air, for example, consists of molecules in which two oxygen atoms are bound together, and for this reason it is written in chemical notation as O_2 and not O. Similarly, gaseous NITROGEN and CHLORINE, N_2 and Cl_2 respectively, are composed of molecules each having two atoms. On the other hand the INERT GASES such as argon, Ar, are made up of atoms and not molecules.

Chemical compounds are usually regarded as being composed of a collection of identical molecules. Thus water, H_2O, contains molecules having two atoms of hydrogen each bonded to a single oxygen atom, and the HYDROCARBON methane, CH_4, has a central carbon atom bonded to four hydrogen atoms. While this concept is a good way to look at many compounds, particularly organic compounds, it does not give a correct picture of the structure where the chemical bonding is ionic (electrovalent). Sodium chloride, for example, is written in chemical notation as NaCl because it contains sodium IONS and chloride ions in the ratio 1:1, but it does not contain discrete molecules in which a single sodium ion is bound to a single chloride ion. Rather, the sodium ions and the chloride ions are distributed uniformly throughout a CRYSTAL lattice in which each sodium ion is surrounded by six equally spaced chloride ions and each chloride ion is surrounded by six equally spaced sodium ions; a particular chloride ion in the crystal lattice cannot be said to 'belong' to any single sodium ion.

Some molecules, for example PROTEINS, are extremely complex and the elucidation of their structure has proved correspondingly difficult. Techniques used for structure determination include both chemical methods and physical methods, for example infra-red SPECTROSCOPY, NUCLEAR MAGNETIC RESONANCE, MASS SPECTROSCOPY and X-ray CRYSTALLOGRAPHY.

Molecular weight

The *atomic weight* of an element is a measure of the weight of one atom of the element as compared to the weight of a carbon atom which is arbitrarily taken to be 12. The *molecular weight* of a compound is simply the sum of the atomic weights of the atoms contained in a single molecule and can therefore easily be calculated from its molecular formula: the molecular weight of benzene, C_6H_6, is 78 (the atomic weight of hydrogen is 1), the molecular weight of water, H_2O, is 18 (the atomic weight of oxygen is 16), and so on. Conversely, knowledge of the molecular weight of an unknown compound is a useful guide to its atomic composition.

The Italian chemist Amedeo AVOGADRO discovered in 1811 that the same volume of different gases will contain the same number of molecules at standard temperature and pressure (0°C and 760 mm Hg respectively). It was determined experimentally that the molecular weight in grammes of a gaseous compound (for example 16 grammes of methane, CH_4) occupies 22.4 litres at standard temperature and pressure (STP). By determining the density of a gas under appropriate conditions and working out the weight that would occupy 22.4 litres at STP, its molecular weight can be calculated.

Another method of determining molecular weight relies on the fact that when a compound is dissolved in a liquid, the boiling point of the liquid is raised and its melting point is lowered. The amount by which the boiling point is raised or the melting point lowered for a given weight of the dissolved substance is inversely proportional to its molecular weight;

in other words the lower the molecular weight, the more the boiling point is raised or melting point lowered.

MOMENT OF INERTIA (see inertia)

MOMENTUM (see dynamics)

MONOLITHIC CHIP CIRCUITS (see integrated circuits)

MONOTYPE (see Linotype)

Below: a model showing the shape of a myoglobin molecule. It is an oxygen-containing compound found in muscle fibres and consists of an iron-containing part and a protein part (white).

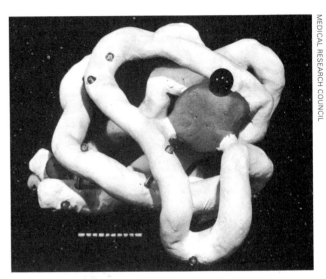

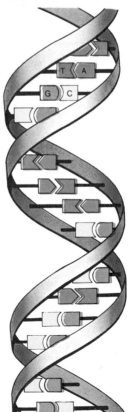

PROF M H F WILKINS/KING'S COLLEGE, LONDON

Below: a model of a deoxyribonucleic acid (DNA) molecule. The molecule is composed of two helical strands running parallel to each other, each consisting of a chain of nucleoside units linked together with phosphate groups. The molecular weight will depend on the source of the DNA but can be in excess of ten million.
Below left: a diagrammatic view of a nucleic acid molecule. The two helical bands represent chains of nucleotide units, each of which carries one of four bases: adenine (A), thymine (T), cytosine (C) or guanine (G). The two chains are held together by bonding between thymine and adenine, and between cytosine and guanine.

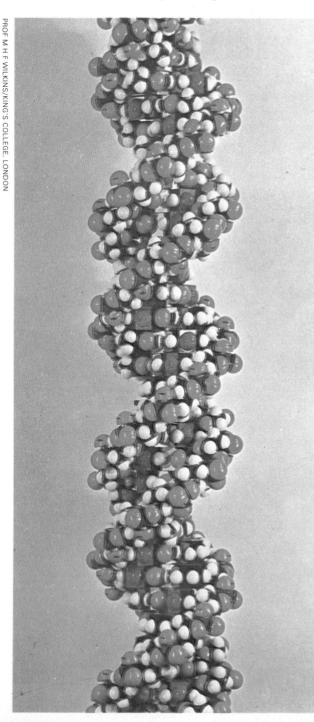

MONORAIL SYSTEMS

Monorails are railways with only one rail instead of two. They have been experimentally built for more than a hundred years; there would seem to be an advantage in that one rail and its sleepers would occupy less space than two, but in practice monorail construction tended to be complicated and unsightly on account of the necessity of keeping the cars upright. There is also the problem of switching the cars from one line to another.

Lartigue systems The first monorails used an elevated rail with the cars hanging down on both sides, like pannier bags [saddle bags] on a pony or a bicycle. A monorail was patented in 1821 by Henry Robinson Palmer, engineer to the London Dock Company, and the first line was built in 1824 to run between the Royal Victualling Yard and the Thames. The elevated wooden rail was a plank on edge bridging strong wooden supports, into which it was set, with an iron bar on top to take the wear from the double-flanged wheels of the cars. A similar line was built to carry bricks to River Lea barges from a brickworks at Cheshunt in 1825. The cars, pulled by a horse and a tow rope, were in two parts, one on each side of the rail, hanging from a framework which carried the wheels.

Later, monorails on this principle were built by a Frenchman, C F M T Lartigue. He put his single rail on top of a series of triangular trestles with their bases on the ground; he also put a guide rail on each side of the trestles on which ran horizontal wheels attached to the cars. The cars thus had both vertical and sideways support and were suitable for higher speeds than the earlier type.

A steam-operated line on this principle was built in Syria in 1869 by J L Hadden. The locomotive had two vertical boilers, one on each side of the pannier-type vehicle.

An electric Lartigue line was opened in central France in 1894, and there were proposals to build a network of them on Long Island in the USA, radiating from Brooklyn. There was a demonstration in London in 1886 on a short line, trains being hauled by a two-boiler Mallet steam locomotive. This had two double-flanged driving wheels running on the raised centre rail and guiding wheels running on tracks on each side of the trestle. Trains were switched from one track to another by moving a whole section of track sideways to line up with

Below: the monorail system designed by George Bennie and built in Scotland in 1930. It was a short experimental line, powered by an aircraft propeller; the noise must have been intolerable.

THE GLASGOW HERALD

another section. In 1888 a line on this principle was laid in Ireland from Listowel to Ballybunion, a distance of $9\frac{1}{2}$ miles; it ran until 1924. There were three locomotives, each with two horizontal boilers hanging one each side of the centre wheels. They were capable of 27 mph ($43\frac{1}{2}$ km/h); the carriages were built with the lower parts in two sections, between which were the wheels.

The Lartigue design was adapted further by F B Behr, who built a three-mile electric line near Brussels in 1897. The monorail itself was again at the top of an 'A' shaped trestle, but there were two balancing and guiding rails on each side, so that although the weight of the car was carried by one rail, there were really five rails in all. The car weighed 55 tons and had two four-wheeled bogies (that is, four wheels in line on each bogie). It was built in England and had motors putting out a total of 600 horsepower. The car ran at 83 mph (134 km/h) and was said to have reached 100 mph (161 km/h) in private trials. It was extensively tested by representatives of the Belgian, French and Russian governments, and Behr came near to success in achieving wide-scale application of his design.

Gyroscopic monorails An attempt to build a monorail with one rail laid on the ground in order to save space led to the use of a GYROSCOPE to keep the train upright. A gyroscope is a rapidly spinning flywheel which resists any attempt to alter the angle of the axis on which it spins.

A true monorail, running on a single rail, was built for military purposes by Louis Brennan, an Irishman who also invented a steerable TORPEDO. Brennan applied for monorail patents in 1903, exhibited a large working model in 1907 and a full-size 22-ton car in 1909–10. It was held upright by two gyroscopes, spinning in opposite directions, and carried 50 people or ten tons of freight.

A similar car carrying only six passengers and a driver was demonstrated in Berlin in 1909 by August Scherl, who had taken out a patent in 1908 and later came to an agreement with Brennan to use his patents also. Both systems allowed the cars to lean over, like bicycles, on curves. Scherl's was an electric car; Brennan's was powered by petrol [gasoline] rather than steam so as not to show any tell-tale smoke when used by the military. A steam-driven gyroscopic system was designed by Peter Schilovsky, a Russian nobleman. This reached only the model stage; it was held upright by a single steam-driven gyroscope placed in the tender.

The disadvantage with gyroscopic monorail systems was

Right: the SAFEGE monorail system, described as an aerial railway, recently constructed in France. The car is suspended from a box made of steel and split on its underside. Each car has two four wheeled bogies; the wheels support the car on the inside of the split box. Each bogie carries two electric traction motors which each drive two wheels by means of a gear assembly. There are also four small horizontal guiding wheels on each bogie.

Below and left: the Lartigue system which ran in Ireland for more than 35 years. There was a pressure-equalizing pipe between the two boilers of the locomotive; the engine ran on three wheels which were 0.75 m (about two feet) in diameter. There were plans to build such a line from Liverpool to Manchester to run 175 km (108 miles) per hour, but they were not carried out. The centre rail weighed 13 kg per running metre (about 26 pounds per yard). Switching was accomplished by swinging a section of rail on a turntable, visible in the picture on the left.

that they required power to drive the gyroscope to keep the train upright even when it was not moving.

Overhead guides Systems were built which ran on single rails on the ground but used a guide rail at the top to keep the train upright. Wheels on top of the train engaged with the guiding rail. The structural support necessary for the guide rail immediately nullified the economy in land use which was the main argument in favour of monorails.

The best known such system was designed by H H Tunis and built by August Belmont. It was $1\frac{1}{2}$ miles long (2.4 m) and ran between Barton Station on the New York, New Haven & Hartford Railroad and City Island (Marshall's Corner) in $1\frac{1}{2}$ minutes. The overhead guide rail was arranged to make the single car lean over on a curve and the line was designed for high speeds. It ran for four months in 1910, but on 17 July of that year the driver took a curve too slowly, the guidance system failed and the car crashed with 100 people on board. It never ran again.

Alweg systems The most successful modern monorails have been the invention of Dr Axel L Wenner-Gren, an industrialist born in Sweden. Alweg lines use a concrete beam carried on concrete supports; the beam can be high in the air, at ground

level or in a tunnel, as required. The cars straddle the beam, supported by rubber-tyred wheels on top of the beam; there are also horizontal wheels in two rows on each side underneath, bearing on the sides of the beam near the top and bottom of it. Thus there are five bearing surfaces, as in the Behr system, but combined to use a single beam instead of a massive steel trestle framework. The carrying wheels come up into the centre line of the cars, suitably enclosed. Electric current is picked up from power lines at the side of the beam. A number of successful lines have been built on the Alweg system, including a line $8\frac{1}{4}$ miles (13.3 km) long between Tokyo and its Haneda airport.

There are several other 'saddle' type systems on the same principle as the Alweg, including a small industrial system used on building sites and for agricultural purposes which can run without a driver. With all these systems, trains are diverted from one track to another by moving pieces of track sideways to bring in another piece of track to form a new link, or by using a flexible section of track to give the same result.

Other systems Another monorail system suspends the car beneath an overhead carrying rail. The wheels must be over the centre line of the car, so the support connected between

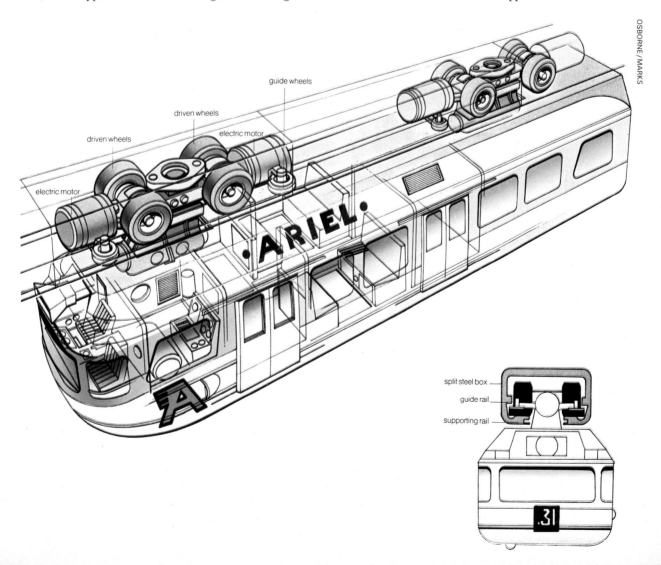

OSBORNE/MARKS

guide wheels

driven wheels

driven wheels

electric motor

electric motor

ARIEL

split steel box

guide rail

supporting rail

.31

rail and car is to one side, or offset. This allows the rail to be supported from the other side. Such a system was built between the towns of Barmen and Elberfeld in Germany in 1898–1901 and was extended in 1903 to a length of 8.2 miles (13 km). It has run successfully ever since, with a remarkable safety record. Tests in the river valley between the towns showed that a monorail would be more suitable than a conventional railway in the restricted space available because monorail cars could take sharper curves in comfort. The rail is suspended on a steel structure, mostly over the River Wupper itself. The switches or points on the line are in the form a switch tongue forming an inclined plane, which is placed over the rail; the car wheels rise on this plane and are thus led on to the siding.

An experimental line using the same principle of suspension, but with the car driven by means of an aircraft propeller, was designed by George Bennie and built at Milngavie (Scotland) in 1930. The line was too short for high speeds, but it was claimed that 200 mph (322 km/h) was possible. There was an auxiliary rail below the car on which horizontal wheels ran to control the sway

A modern system, the SAFEGE developed in France, has suspended cars but with the 'rail' in the form of a steel box section split on the underside to allow the car supports to pass through it. There are two rails inside the box, one on each side of the slot, and the cars are actually suspended from four-wheeled bogies running on the two rails.

Above right: an experimental monorail powered by a jet engine, near Paris.

Above: a monorail at Blackpool, England, built by Habegger Thun of Switzerland.

Right: the most successful monorails have been the Alweg systems, designed by a Swedish industrialist. This is the Tokyo installation, which runs from the airport to the city centre. The Alweg design has five bearing surfaces on a single concrete beam: a rubber wheel runs on top of the beam and two more wheels bear on each side of it. Electric power is picked up from cables on the side of the beam. The Tokyo line is $8\frac{1}{4}$ miles (13·3 km) long.

MORSE, Samuel F B (1791-1872)

Samuel Finley Breese Morse invented a telegraph apparatus, sent the first telegraph signal in the United States, and devised the Morse code, still used for certain kinds of cable transmission. Like Thomas EDISON, he had an intuitive mind rather than great scientific originality; like Robert FULTON, he was a painter as well as an inventor.

Morse was born in Charlestown, Massachusetts. His father was a controversial clergyman who wrote some of the first American books on geography. After graduating from Yale in 1810, Morse received his parents' reluctant permission to pursue a career as an artist, and sailed for England to study painting. Encouraged by his success there, he returned to Boston to set up a studio, hoping to make a living painting historical scenes. The only kind of paintings Americans wanted to buy, however, were portraits, and there were not many commissions even for those. For some years Morse made a precarious living at portraiture.

Between 1825 and 1828, Morse's wife, his mother and his father died. Together with his difficulty making a living as an artist, this was the beginning of a difficult period in his life. In 1829 he sailed for Europe, where he was influenced by some of the stranger political currents of the time in France and Italy. On his return trip in 1832, one of his fellow passengers demonstrated some electrical apparatus, and Morse suddenly became consumed with the idea of transmitting intelligence instantaneously by means of electricity. He outlined in his notebook the three basic elements of a telegraph system: a sending apparatus to transmit by opening and closing a circuit; a receiving device operated by an ELECTRO-MAGNET to record signals as dots and spaces on a strip of paper moved by clockwork; and a code. As he developed his idea, he realized that the code could be read by ear as well as recorded; he added dashes to the dots and spaces and his initial clumsy sending device became a simple sounding key. He did not consider his invention as a means of sending news and personal messages around the world, but as a means of transmitting important and secret government messages; accordingly he spent some time devising a secret code which required the use of a large de-coding book.

This was not Morse's first venture into technology. In 1817, with his brother, he had patented a flexible piston pump for fire engines; in 1822 he had built a marble cutting machine (he was also a sculptor) which unfortunately infringed on an earlier patent. He also experimented with such substances as milk and beer in the grinding of his pigments. While he worked on the telegraph, he continued painting, and, like his father, also indulged in political and religious controversy. He ran for mayor of New York on a Nativist (anti-Catholic) ticket, receiving only 1500 votes.

In 1836 Morse showed his telegraph to his colleague Leonard Dunnell Gale. Morse's difficulty was that his knowledge of electromagnetics was several years out of date; he could not make his apparatus work more than 40 feet (12 m) from his battery. Morse and Gale experimented with wire wound round Gale's lecture room until they could send messages as far as ten miles (16 km). Morse then worked out a system of electromagnetic relays which would enable messages to be sent as far as desired. Similar developments were taking place elsewhere, notably in England, but a document filed in 1837 shows that the American research was original. In that year Morse reluctantly gave up painting and sailed for Europe again. He was honoured by scientists in France, but he could not obtain patents there or in England.

In 1843, a busy US Congress in a hurry to adjourn voted money for a telegraph experiment. A line was set up between Washington DC and nearby Baltimore; on 24 May 1844, Morse sent the famous message 'What hath God wrought' from the Supreme Court room; it was returned accurately and a short conversation followed. Morse wanted to sell the invention outright to the government and go back to painting, but the postmaster general at the time thought that the telegraph would never pay, so its development was left in private hands.

In 1854 Morse ran for Congress as a Democrat and was defeated. In 1857-58 he worked as an electrician for Cyrus W Field, who was laying transatlantic cables, but resigned because of company intrigue. He correctly predicted the failure of the second cable because of inadequate insulation.

After many years of struggle and relative poverty, Morse finally became a wealthy man because of his American patents. He was lucky in his choice of financial advisor, despite litigation with his enemies and his own capacity for being swindled. European governments showered him with honours, but continued to deny him patents. He was married twice and had eight children; his youngest son graduated from Yale more than sixty years after he did. When Morse died in 1872, the Congress paid tribute to his technical achievement but ignored his painting; since an exhibition of his painting in New York in 1932, he has been given credit for his influence on American art as well as his achievement in communications.

Below left: Daguerreotype portrait of Samuel Morse, American portrait painter and inventor of the telegraph.

Below right: Morse's first telegraph apparatus, patented in 1837. In the foreground is the sending device; in the background the receiver, mounted on a wooden frame.

Bottom: receiver of Morse printing telegraph, c 1890.

MORTAR, building

The kiln burned bricks used to build the ziggurats at Ur, about 2000 BC were bonded with bitumen, and it was not until the first century BC that durable building mortars were developed through the expertise of the Romans. In his writings Vitruvius gave detailed accounts of the burning and slaking (addition of water) of lime and the proportions in which it should be mixed with sand for plastering and stucco, as well as the preparation and use of hydraulic CEMENT (*pozzolana*), which was incorporated into both mortar and concrete mixtures.

The mortar used in northern Europe, during the mediaeval and later periods, consisted of lime and sand, but because lime burning and the proportions of lime in the mixture were not as scientifically controlled as with the Romans, much of the mortar in stonework from this period is in a dangerous crumbly state.

Modern mortars

Nowadays mortars are used for a variety of building jobs including plastering, rendering and masonry bonding, providing weatherproof joints and surfaces. Basically they are putty-like mixtures of cement, sand and water; often they include lime or a mortar plasticizer to improve the workability. The proportions, however, in a mixture depend on the type of construction work involved. Lime helps to provide a 'fatty' consistency so that the mortar both clings and spreads; it also helps the mortar to retain water so that it does not set too rapidly but gradually stiffens as the water is lost through evaporation and absorption into the adjoining masonry. The lime also assists the mortar to absorb local strains without accumulation of movement. Plasticizers are useful with low cement and sand mixtures and work by enclosing air in the mixture thereby helping the binder paste to fill up any gaps in the sand.

Coloured mortars are obtained by grinding between 5 and 10% of a pigment together with the cement.

Mixtures

The type of mortar most frequently used for plastering is cement, lime and sand in the proportions (by volume) 1:1:6 or 1:2:9; each is suitable as an undercoat on most types of background and provide strong hard surfaces suitable for damp conditions. They may also be textured and are applied with a wooden float. Alternatively, cement and sand plasters having similar qualities may be used.

For rendering external surfaces two coats are generally needed and often finishes such as pebbledash, roughcast or texturing are incorporated where a wall is likely to be very exposed to bad weather. As with plastering, succeeding coats should be weaker than the preceding ones. Proportions of cement, lime and sand may vary from $1:0-\frac{1}{4}:3$ to $1:2:9$ depending on whether the rendering is an undercoat or a final coat and the type of finish incorporated.

In bricklaying a variety of mortar mixtures are used depending on the type of brickwork such as outside free-standing walls, window sills and inner walls. Mortar mixtures for cement, lime and sand formulations range from $1:0-\frac{1}{4}:3$ to $1:3:12$. Better frost resistance, however, is provided by mortars consisting of cement and sand with a plasticizer. Batches of mortar can be proportioned by weight or frequently by volume and are normally mixed by hand in sufficient quantities to be used up within two hours.

An example of the durability of the mortars made by the Romans can be seen in this wall at Verulamium (now St Albans, England) of rubble and flint with brick lacing courses.

After the decline of the Romans, the art of making strong weatherproof mortars declined. The mediaeval lime and sand mixtures were weaker and in time became crumbly.

Concrete blocks are bedded in a modern plasticized cement and sand mortar. The plasticizer works by trapping air in the mix so that the binder paste fills any gaps.

MORTAR, military

A mortar is a high trajectory fire weapon in which the recoil force is passed directly to the ground by means of a baseplate. The conventional mortar, as used by the armies of most countries, is muzzle loading and has a smooth bore. It fires a fin stabilized projectile at subsonic velocity, and establishes zones of fire by variation of the charge weight. Range is adjusted by altering the elevation. The high trajectory of a mortar allows the weapon to be placed behind hills, in valleys or in small steep sided pits, and to engage troops in trenches, sunken roads or behind cover.

The mortar was one of the earliest forms of artillery and is known to have been used by Mohammed II at the time of the siege of Constantinople in 1453. It was known in Europe as the *bombard* and consisted of a metal pot secured to a timber base. It was used for attacking fortresses and cities under siege and also for action against ships close to shore. There was also a naval equivalent. The bombard fell out of favour as other forms of artillery developed (see CANNON and GUN) and did not come into prominence again until World War 1, when Sir Wilfred Stokes produced a mortar of 3 inch (7.6 cm) diameter, a calibre which is still in favour today. Probably the largest mortar ever produced was the 'Little David' mortar which was built in 1944 for the US army. It had a 36 inch (914 mm) calibre and fired a projectile weighing 3700 lb (1678 kg).

Construction The great majority of mortars have four main parts: the *barrel*, the *baseplate*, the *mount* and the *sight*. The barrel is a smooth bore steel tube, and the exterior is also usually smooth, although some mortars incorporate radial finning to assist cooling. The FIRING MECHANISM is incorporated in a breech piece which is usually screwed into the base of the barrel. In many cases the firing mechanism is a simple stud which sets off the propellant charge of the mortar bomb by impact as soon as the latter has fallen to the lower end of the barrel after loading. In some mortars, however, the firing mechanism is a spring operated device controlled by an external trigger. The baseplate is designed to distribute the downward force of the propellant explosion over as large an area as possible to prevent the mortar from being driven downwards into the ground. The mounting is normally a bipod, but occasionally a tripod is used. The mounting supports the barrel and carries the *elevating* and *traversing* mechanisms which are used for aiming. In many mortars a shock absorber is incorporated in the mounting, and this usually consists of one or two cylinders containing springs, although in some heavier mortars a hydraulic system may be employed. These cylinders are interposed between the barrel collar and the bipod, and after the barrel has recoiled and been pushed back by the reaction of the baseplate, the springs ensure that the barrel returns.

The bipod carries a *cross levelling* device which enables the sights to be kept upright regardless of the slope of the ground on which the mortar is situated. Mortar sights have increased in complexity as the years have passed. Initially they were very simple and consisted of an *aiming tube* and a flat plate, which allowed the gunner to relate the direction in which the mortar was pointing to some arbitrarily selected reference point. The modern mortar sight allows the target bearing to be determined and also allows the range and bearing to be recorded so that once a target has been attacked, it can be re-engaged without going through the entire ranging process again.

Characteristics Mortars range in calibre from less than 60 mm (2.4 inch) for light mortars to above 100 mm (3.9 inch) for heavy mortars. A light mortar fires a projectile weighing from 1 to 3 lb (0.45 to 1.36 kg) to a maximum range of between 500 and 2000 yards or metres. Heavy mortars have a maximum range of about 10,000 yards or metres and fire a projectile weighing 15 lb (6.8 kg) or more.

The limited number of components and the relative simplicity of the fire control system make the mortar easy to handle and reduce training time. Mortars are cheap and easy to produce. The simple design of the mortar and its sight allows rapid switches of target anywhere within a 360° arc, and the low pressure within the mortar chamber means that a thin walled bomb with a relatively large high explosive content can be used. This, combined with the near vertical angle of projectile descent, provides a good all round fragmentation and makes the mortar more effective against troops in the open than the artillery gun. The advantages are, however, offset to some extent by the fact that mortars are less accurate than guns.

MOTION (see dynamics)

MOTOR, ELECTRIC (see electric motor)

Top: Mallet's 36 inch (91 cm) mortar of 1857. It was capable of firing a projectile weighing 1 ton to 2760 yards (2314 m).

Above left: a 2 inch (5.1 cm) World War 1 trench mortar. The spherical head of the projectile is filled with high explosive, and an impact fuze can be seen projecting from its front end. The mortar was fired by a blank cartridge which was loaded into a rifle firing mechanism at the lower end of the barrel.

Above right: a modern 81 mm (3.2 inch) mortar. It is operated by a two or three man crew and has a maximum range of 4500 m (4900 yd).

MOTORCYCLE

The first motorcycles, built at the beginning of this century, were essentially pedal cycles to which crude INTERNAL COMBUSTION ENGINES had been added to assist the rider. Frequently, the rider had to assist the engine. (Nowadays, motorized pedal cycles, called *mopeds*, are used throughout the world; the engines are small but so efficient that the pedals are retained only for starting and to take advantage of licence tax concessions.)

Before World War 1, motorcycles had achieved speed and stamina as a result of intensive development for racing. The frame became heavier, the seat was lowered, the front forks incorporated springing to protect the rider from road shocks, and the engine was mounted where the pedal cranks had been previously. Though in some cases the engine still turned the wheels by means of V-belts running in pulley wheels, up-to-date machines already had a GEARBOX providing two or three gear ratios between the engine and the rear wheel, a friction CLUTCH, and power transmission by means of roller chains (see CHAIN DRIVE). The final refinement was a *kick starter*, a single pedal crank which enabled the rider to start the engine without having to push the machine.

Between the wars this basic design was improved in detail and performance, and Britain dominated the motorcycle industry with well constructed machines of conservative design. The most popular type of machine had a one-cylinder engine; attempts to market more advanced designs with four-cylinder engines and shaft power transmission met with commercial failure.

Since World War 2 the motorcycle has become more popular than ever for transport and sport. After brief periods of influence by Britain, Italy and Germany, Japan emerged as the major producer of motorcycles, building highly developed designs in greater numbers than ever seen before, as greater prosperity in emergent nations made personal transport attainable. Japanese success stimulated design in Europe, with the result that the range of machines available is greater than ever.

Modern motorcycles

Today motorcycles are built in sizes ranging from 50 cc (engine displacement expressed in cubic centimetres) models for beginners to 1000 cc and over for experts. Most motorcycles have two or three cylinders, except for small inexpensive models; a few have four cylinders and six-cylinder models have also been built. Rotary engined models are in the experimental stage (see WANKEL ENGINE).

Almost every machine has hydraulically damped springing for both wheels, which has greatly improved safe handling and road holding qualities; many other features have been taken from car design. Electric starters are provided on the more expensive models, together with disc BRAKES, in which friction pads are pressed by hydraulic pressure against a steel disc on the wheel, and flashing turn indicators. Instrumentation in general follows car practice, with matched speedometer and engine revolution counter (tachometer) and warning lights to monitor lubrication and electrical systems. Purchase and running costs frequently approach car levels; the more advanced machines cost more than a small car and compare unfavourably in fuel consumption. The attraction to the user is speed, 120 mph (193 km/h) being obtainable with stock machines and 150 mph (241 km/h) or more for racing models.

Transmission (gearbox) design is peculiar to motorcycles. Four gears are normal and the trend is to five or six. No synchromesh is supplied or demanded; a ratchet mechanism provides gear changes up or down one at a time by means of foot pressure on a gear pedal. It is much quicker and more positive than manual gearbox operation in a car.

Engines

Motorcycle engines employing the four-stroke principle with a power stroke on alternate revolutions use a circulatory lubrication system similar to that on a car. Two-stroke engines are lubricated by mixing a small amount of oil with the petrol [gasoline], but these engines are available only on the cheaper utility models.

Development of engine design has resulted in machines of 250 cc capacity with more power than the largest machines of a few years ago, and machines up to this size are the most popular for road use. Four-cylinder models are built on racing engine lines, with the valves operated by overhead camshafts to enable them to run at speeds of as high as 10,000 rpm. In the case of two-stroke engines, rotary valves and vibrating reed valves are frequently employed to improve efficiency.

Specialized designs

The popularity of cross country motorcycle racing (called *motocross*) has resulted in *trail* machines, designed for off-road use, including increased ground clearance, lower gear ratios and deeply studded tyres.

Streamlined coverings are used on some road racing

Top left: a brightly painted 'tricycle' (motorcycle with sidecar) used as a taxi in Manila, Philippines.

Below left: an early attempt to build a motorized cycle. This one was built by Daimler in 1885. A belt from the motor drives a small gear inside a large annulus gear on the rear wheel.

Below: the Moby X-1, a small motor scooter which is more or less portable. Such vehicles are convenient for getting from place to place in cities, which are choking with motor car traffic.

Right: a sidecar scramble through a muddy field. Purpose built motorcycles can go nearly anywhere and have been used in wartime.

A modern motorcycle. Motorcycles today, as compared with those of World War I vintage, have lower seats, heavier frames and shock absorbers front and rear. These developments make the machines much safer than they were, by lowering the centre of gravity, giving more structural stability and providing better handling qualities. The clutch and gearbox operation is quicker and more positive than that of a motor car. Disc brakes and instrumentation such as tachometers and turning indicators are among the further refinements which have helped to make motorcycling more popular than ever for transport and sport.

carb

dynamo

oil tank

rear shock absorber

chain case

chain drive

swinging arm frame

adjusters

footrest

kick start

ge

stand

JOHN BISHOP

steering damper

petrol tank

rocker box   tappet

rocker shaft

cylinder head

exhaust valve

twist throttle

brake lever

front spring units

exhaust port

pushrod

piston

cylinder block

fuel lines

cooling fins

tachometer drive

front brake

timing case

crank case

main oil feed

clutch actuator

gear change pedal

machines to reduce wind drag. Cigar shaped projectiles, sometimes fitted with two engines and enclosing the driver completely, have attained speeds of more than 250 mph (400 km/h), but their only resemblance to a motorcycle is in the disposition of the two wheels.

At the other end of the scale, variants with small wheels and footboards instead of pedal rests are called *motor scooters*. These often have shields to protect the driver from dirt from the road or from the machine.

Once popular on the road, the motorcycle sidecar, a passenger carrying attachment with its own load-bearing wheel, is rarely seen nowadays, but the wheel arrangement is used in specialized passenger machine racing.

Controls Motorcycle controls have become standardized. Throttle control is effected by rotating the grip on the right handlebar. On the same handlebar is a lever for operating the front brake; on the other handlebar is a lever which operates the clutch. To satisfy international driving rules, the pedal operating the gear change is usually on the left side of the machine, and a pedal on the other side operates the rear brake. Switch controls for the electric lamps are fitted to the handlebars. Most machines have two stands, a prop stand for parking and a centre stand which lifts the wheels off the ground for maintenance work.

MOVIE CAMERA (see camera, movie)

Below: a BMW (Bavarian Motor Works) 900 cc motorcycle, with disc brakes, turn indicators, twin rear view mirrors and other extras.

MOVIE FILM PRODUCTION

The production of a motion picture film is a long and complicated process involving a wide range of techniques and equipment. The screenplay which sets out the film as it will appear on the screen is broken down into shots in the shooting script, carrying instructions for the technicians including such details as whether it is to be a long, medium or close shot.

It is invariably necessary to shoot a film out of screenplay order. Scenes requiring the same location or set (in a studio) or a particularly highly paid performer will be grouped together for shooting purposes. The normal film making procedure is to use only one camera. A scene is therefore shot many times from different camera positions to create different points of view and types of shot (long shots, close ups, for example). These separate shots may overlap to varying degrees to allow a choice at the later editing stage. There will also be different takes of each shot.

Left: on rare occasions more than one camera is used. A spectacular staged crash, or a location car scene such as this where continuity raises problems are examples. An alternative here would be to project the outside views on to screens outside a stationary car— not very realistic. A more typical location arrangement is shown below left: note the camera dolly for smooth tracking shots.

Below: a Steenbeck machine for editing 16 mm film, enabling one film (at rear) and two sound tracks to be run in complete synchronization either continuously or frame by frame.

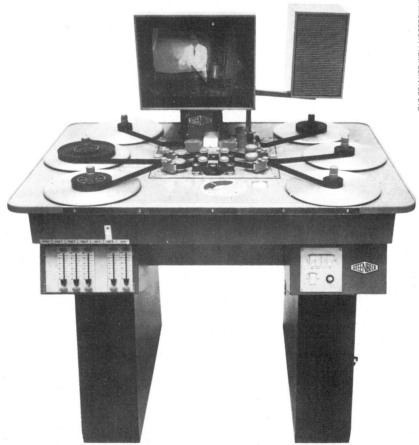

The film in the CAMERA is normally 35 mm colour negative, giving a picture size of 0.87×0.63 inch (22×16 mm). The camera runs at 24 frames (single pictures) per second. The sound is recorded on ordinary ¼ inch (6.5 mm) magnetic tape using TAPE RECORDERS usually running at 7½ inches per second (19 cm/sec). The exact speed of the camera and tape recorder are controlled by a system of pulses which are recorded on the tape to guarantee the correct speed of the magnetic film on to which the sound is transferred later. This magnetic film has a clear base of the same dimensions and with the same sprocket holes as the picture film but is coated with a metal oxide like magnetic tape. To identify each shot and to provide a synchronization (sync) point for the lining up of sound and picture later, a *clapper board* is shot at the front of each take. When lining the two up ('syncing'), the picture frame where the two halves of the board meet are synchronized with the first modulation of the corresponding bang on the track.

The day's shooting, known as the *rushes*, is viewed in a movie theatre the following morning to check the performance and picture quality. The laboratory has developed the negative overnight and made rush prints from it. The rushes are not graded: that is, they may show variations in colour cast and density.

Editing   The editor will view the film on an editing machine of the Movieola or Steenbeck type, capable of running the picture in perfect sync with the sound (now on 35 mm magnetic film) both forwards and backwards at various speeds and frame by frame. To keep picture and sound in sync during editing, they are always kept in a synchronizer (up to four sprocketed wheels in parallel on the same shaft) when cutting. The cuts are made on a tape joiner, consisting of a block for joining and a knife edge for cutting. All the joins are made with clear sticky

tape so that alterations can easily be made. Gradually the 'cutting copy' is built up until the director and producer are satisfied. The soundtrack will be incomplete, consisting mainly of dialogue without music and effects. Dialogue will often be re-recorded by post-synchronization using short sections of scenes as loops. This way the artistes can recreate their performance while hearing and watching the original, and a better quality recording made. Sound effects will often be specially recorded.

The sound editor will make up music and effects tracks and prepare them for the final 'dub' when all the different elements will be mixed together. He may also dub a special music and effects track (M & E track) for foreign sales. The local distributors will dub in the dialogue in the required language.

The camera negative is stored in the laboratory while the editing takes place. During this period it will be decided what optical effects are required. One scene can dissolve into another, and scenes be superimposed on each other if need be. In the same way, rain or lightning may be optically added. This is done on an optical printer, which may have the two separate shots to be combined running simultaneously, with a system of half silvered mirrors making it possible to project them both on to duplicating film. A shutter can control the brightness of each separate shot, making it possible to produce fades and crossfades (dissolves). The same type of printer may be used for adding superimposed titles. To allow freedom to experiment in making such optical effects, duplicates are made from the original negative which can then be kept safe. One can make an interpositive from the original negative, and a negative from that, or alternatively, a CRI (colour reversal intermediate) can be made producing a duplicate negative in one process, at lower cost but of poorer quality.

A computer turns Groucho Marx into Elvis Presley. By either scanning the pictures photoelectrically, as in this case, or by using a tracing device, the likenesses at either end are turned into numbers. The computer then changes the numbers in a smooth sequence to alter the pictures.

The duplicates are made either on an optical printer projecting the image on to the duplicating stock, or on a contact printer bringing the two stocks into contact with their emulsion sides facing each other. Contact printers usually have the two stocks moving continuously over a light source (continuous printer), while optical printers can be combined continuous printers and step printers (working frame by frame).

When the cutting copy has been finalized incorporating optical effects, the negatives (original and optical effects) are cut to match it. This is simplified by key numbers exposed on to the edge of the film during manufacture and thus transferred to the cutting copy in the rush printing. The negative is spliced with film cement.

The mixed SOUNDTRACK will have been transferred to a film negative, the sound being photographically recorded along the edge of the film. This track is called an optical sound negative. In some cases, the soundtrack may be recorded directly on to a magnetic 'stripe' alongside the picture area.

Grading The picture negative is then viewed on a colour video analyzer (see COLOUR PRINT MAKING) by the grader, who will be able to determine the colour and density corrections to be introduced in the making of the first 'married print' with both sound and picture. After seeing this first *answer print*, smaller corrections will usually be made before release printing will start. To preserve the original cut negative, a graded CRI is often made and the release prints made from this.

If large bulk orders are expected it may be desirable to use the Technicolor process. This is not strictly a photographic process, but a dye transfer process using matrices in the form of 'separation' black and white prints. These are made from the colour negative, each through a different colour filter, producing a gelatin record of the respective cyan, magenta and yellow content of the original image. These matrices are then saturated with the corresponding dye and mechanically printed on to a clear gelatin coated film. Making one matrix for each of the three colours give greater control in the final dye transfer print.

Animation Cartoons and animated films are made frame by frame. Usually 12 drawings have to be prepared for each second of film, each being photographed twice. In most cases the background and some part of the character remains constant, while only a small part of the picture—head, legs or arms—is altered for every other frame. This is made easy by painting the moving part on a series of transparent overlays ('cels') which are then in turn placed in accurate register against the character's body and background, and the frame exposure is made. Complex actions such as running are drawn as cycles making it possible to use each cel repeatedly. The sound for a cartoon is usually recorded first and the soundtrack is analyzed frame by frame on a Movieola. This analysis is used by the animator to decide the number of frames to be taken for each piece of action. All the information about the artwork to be shot is listed on a 'dope sheet' which is given to the animation camera operator together with all the artwork. Small COMPUTERS have been used for some time in helping to compute the camera moves and also to control the SERVOMOTORS effecting these moves.

It is also possible to use computers to help with the animation itself. The animator will only have to draw the key drawings and major in-betweens, (say, every sixth image). The computer will determine the smooth movement of each component line in the character from one position to the next in the required number of steps. This technique presupposes that the movement can be mathematically formulated.

Films can also be made using models which are moved slightly from one frame to the next. Similar techniques are used with actors to create 'impossible' special effects, such as an unlikely 'hole in one' during a comedy golf sequence. People can also be made to disappear from the middle of the scene by stopping the camera while the actor moves out of view. Any other actors must keep perfectly still until the camera starts again.

MOVIE PROJECTOR (see projector)

MUFFLER (see exhaust systems)

RANK FILM LABORATORIES

Far left: a video colour negative analyzer, for grading films. A grey scale is included on the film when shooting as a colour check.

Left: a computerized animation stand. The cels are laid on the motorized baseboard, which is controlled by an analog computer.

Right: this optical printer is being used to superimpose a previously photographed title in colour on a moving background.

MUSICAL BOX

A musical box is a device for the mechanical production of music and belongs to the class of instruments called *ideophones* —instruments that produce sound by themselves. Although the term musical box is often applied loosely to other types of self-acting musical instrument such as the *organette*, *serinette* and *singing bird*, the real musical box relies for its sound on the tones produced by plucking tuned steel tongues, or teeth, arranged like a comb.

The process of plucking is carried out in one of two ways. The first is the cylinder movement, in which the teeth are plucked by being brought into direct contact with a series of short steel pins arranged in the surface of a slowly-rotating metal cylinder or barrel. The second is the disc-playing movement in which the teeth are plucked by projections or perforations, arranged in the surface of a slowly-revolving metal disc, by means of a small revolving multi-pointed starwheel.

Cylinder machines Initially, the musical movement was a very small piece of craftsmanship intended for use in a pocket watch and, before the invention of the plucked steel tooth system, the only means of providing such music was by the use of hammers and small bells, nested one inside the other. This made for a bulky watch with a scale of only a few notes.

In the early part of 1796, a watchmaker named Antoine Favre (1767–1828) reported to the Geneva Society of Arts that he had 'succeeded in establishing carillons without bells or hammers'. Favre's invention was to use a tuned steel tooth plucked, in the earliest examples, either by pins set in a flat wheel, or by projections set in the outer surface of the spring barrel. Because these tiny movements often formed part of some other work, such as a watch, gold vinaigrette or even a seal, they are extremely rare and valuable. Musically, their performance is poor, yet in them can be recognized the beginnings of what was to be a major industry for almost a century.

While the earliest pieces were built exclusively by watchmakers in the Swiss Jura, the next 20 years saw the steady development of the technique of the musical movement and a handful of craftsmen began to concentrate on this offshoot of watchmaking. The art spread north-east from the Jura right up to the Bavarian hinterland of Baden, and south-west along the Vallée de Jour as far as Brassus. Geneva became the centre of trade, and musical boxes were manufactured there after 1840.

From its early beginnings as a novelty addition to a time-piece, the musical mechanism gradually became an instrument in its own right and by 1820 or so, instead of the musical movement being hidden in the base of a clock to play on the hour, it became elevated to the status of being a solo instrument within its own case. At a time when almost every home in the land possessed a piano, the musical box became an amusement for the well-to-do. Boxes were expensive, and it was not until Paillard established the first factory and went in for mass-production techniques in 1875 that they became comparatively cheap.

The music played on the earlier boxes was of three distinct types: operatic, hymns and psalms, and popular airs. Examples built in this early epoch were almost without exception of high quality with superbly-arranged music. Manufacturers such as Ducommun Girod, Lecoultre, Falconnet et Reymond, Capt. Alibert, Nicole Frères and, a little later, Bremond and Greiner produced work which today demonstrates not only beauty but musical mastery as well. Sadly, the majority of surviving boxes found on the market today comprise those built between the years of about 1870 and the outbreak of

Left: a disc-type musical box by Polyphon of Leipzig.

Below left: the jewel-mounted speed regulating device which ensures constant speed of the cylinder. In this picture the cylinder is turning, the speed regulator is spinning and a pinion is turning with the cylinder which will stop it at the end of the tune.

Above: a cylinder music box with drums and bells, by Dawkins of Geneva. Some mechanical movements had fiddles or horns as well.

Below: a cylinder-type musical box. The tuned tines of the comb, left, are plucked by the pins or wires on the revolving cylinder. The cylinder played from four to twelve tunes.

barrel

pins

prongs

World War I, by which time quality had been overtaken by commercialism.

Disc machines Much of the reason for this was due to the competition provided by the disc-playing musical box, which offered definite advantages over the cylinder box. Whereas the cylinder played from four to 12 tunes (some costly musical boxes were built with interchangeable cylinders which could play a considerably wider choice), the disc box could play an endless variety of tunes. All but the very simplest cylinder boxes were expensive and offered no more musical variety than was to be found on their cylinders.

The disc-playing musical box was invented jointly by a Londoner, Ellis Parr, and a Leipzig industrialist, Paul Lochmann, in the year 1885. It at once made possible the ownership of an enormous repertoire of music since, like a gramophone, the instrument could play whatever discs its owner chose.

The first disc musical box, called the *Symphonion*, came on the market in 1885, but serious production did not start until three years later. Meanwhile, two senior employees of Lochmann's factory, Gustav Brachhausen and Paul Riessner, left and established a rival factory close by to produce the *Polyphon* which not only surpassed the success of the *Symphonion* but became almost a generic term for the disc-playing musical box. Disc boxes were an immediate success. With both *Polyphon* and *Symphonion* in Leipzig, the Swiss tried to meet the competition head on by introducing their own brands such as the *Britannia* and later, the technically superior *Stella* with its smooth, projectionless discs.

Disc instruments were produced with names such as *Monopol*, *Orphenion*, *Euphonia*, *Helvetia* (Swiss), *Sirion* and *Fortuna*. Models ranged from tiny hand-cranked *manivelles* playing discs about four inches (10 cm) in diameter up to giants such as the *Komet*, whose huge clockwork motor turned a disc almost three feet (1 m) across. Meanwhile, Brachhausen crossed the Atlantic to America and in the New Jersey town of Rahway established the Regina Music Box Company. Using Polyphon technology he produced some of the most acoustically advanced disc musical boxes, which were sold in America, England and Germany. Not only aimed at the domestic market, the disc box was also available with coin operation for use in public places.

As the disc-playing musical box spelled the end of the quality cylinder musical box, events of the 20th century marked the end of the disc machine. The phonograph invented by Thomas EDISON could do the one thing of which the musical box was incapable: it could reproduce the human voice. PLAYER PIANOS, player organs and radio finally replaced the musical box altogether.

In the intervening 60 years, the musical box industry of Switzerland has continued to mass-produce small, cheap musical movements for use in novelties. As musical interpreters, these cannot rank with the pieces produced a hundred and more years ago. Recently, however, a line of hand-built quality cylinder musical boxes has emerged and one maker, Reuge, is currently making a small number of expensive and tonally pleasing pieces. During the summer of 1974, a Cologne manufacturer began production of a facsimile of an 1890s disc-playing musical box which sounds indistinguishable from the original. While these demonstrations of a resurgence in the art are interesting, the importance of the instrument as a means of preserving music and bringing music to the masses has passed.

MUSICAL INSTRUMENTS (see various types)

MUSICAL SCALES

Musical tones are sounds with a definite *pitch*, a quality dependent on the rate of acoustical vibration, or *frequency*, and enabling us to relate notes to one another in terms of their 'height'. When the notes used in music are tabulated systematically in ascending or descending order of pitch, they make a musical scale. The *intervals* or leaps of pitch between successive notes vary in different musical systems, and it is primarily these relationships between pitches that characterize a type of music, not the specific underlying frequencies.

The octave There are many scale systems or *modes*, including some oddities with notes more closely spaced than in conventional Western music. But the majority share certain basic intervals, the most important of which is the *octave*. This is the pitch span representing a halving or doubling of frequency. It is a curiosity of our hearing that at each leap of one octave we seem to hear the same note again—of higher or lower pitch but nevertheless merging perfectly with the original note spaced an octave away. This fusion of tones whenever the frequency is doubled has ensured that in all musical systems the pattern of intervals comprising a particular mode is accommodated within an octave, any such scheme being repeated identically within adjacent octaves, just as the seven white notes and five black notes are repeated along a PIANO keyboard.

Pentatonic scale The blending of tones spaced by octaves is an example of *consonance*, a psychological effect repeated in rather less definite form with some other pairs of notes. An octave corresponds to a frequency ratio of 2:1, but notes with a ratio of 3:2 or 4:3 also blend very pleasingly to form simple chords, and these two intervals coexist with the octave in most scale systems. In fact, the three together provide a complete set of notes for the common *pentatonic scale*, used in the East and found in much surviving Western folk music. This can be plotted on to the modern *stave* (or *staff*), where the various intervals are given as frequency ratios of the higher to the lower note.

As such ratios are difficult for non-mathematical people to remember, pitch intervals are usually named in terms of their spacing on the stave. Thus the interval of 3:2 occurs over a span of five possible note positions (inclusive) and is known as a *perfect-fifth* (or simply 'fifth'), that of 4:3 covers four positions and is a *perfect-fourth* ('fourth'), while a ratio of 2:1 spans eight note spaces and is therefore an 'eighth' or octave. These and some other important intervals are shown in the table, together with their frequency ratios, musical character, and positions in modern Western scales. Note that the arithmetically least simple ratios, involving a small step either from unison or from the octave, produce *dissonance*, an objectionable effect opposite to consonance.

Returning to the pentatonic pattern, the group of three notes followed by a gap and then a further pair resembles the layout of black keys on a piano, and indeed the scale shown here as CDEGA (which can be played directly on the white notes) may be duplicated on the black notes of a piano starting from F-sharp. The pitches are different, but because the interval relationships are retained the 'Chinese' musical effect is the same. Much oriental music is pentatonic.

Scales such as this were common in the ancient world and provided the foundations on which Western music was built. The Greeks were fascinated by the mathematics of music and endeavoured to construct scale systems which fitted their beliefs about numbers. They lacked our present knowledge of SOUND with its concepts of frequency and WAVE MOTION, but were well aware of the relationship between size and pitch for plucked strings and primitive WOODWIND INSTRUMENTS. Pythagoras (6th century BC) constructed a scale placing special emphasis on the interval of a fifth, and demonstrated that a step upwards of a fifth followed by a fourth equals an octave ($\frac{3}{2} \times \frac{4}{3} = \frac{12}{6} = 2$). This may be shown on the stave, where note No. 4 in the pentatone (G) is a fifth up from the first note (C) and a fourth below the octave note (upper-C). The same procedure can apply in reverse, moving down in pitch by a fifth and then a fourth from upper- to middle-C ($\frac{2}{3} \times \frac{3}{4} = \frac{1}{2}$), which would fill in the 'missing' note around F. Such manoeuvres create note-by-note steps equal to the difference between a fourth and a fifth ($\frac{3}{2} \div \frac{4}{3} = \frac{9}{8}$), and this *whole-tone* ratio of 9:8 was used by Pythagoras to fill in the finer detail of his scales.

SCALA

Top: two octaves of piano or organ keyboard. Major diatonic scale may be played on white keys starting at C, basic minor scale on white keys starting at A and pentatonic scale on black keys starting at F-sharp. All scales can start from any note by using a suitable selection of black and white keys. Modern tuning to 'concert pitch' places the A above middle C at 440 Hz. Doubling the tension of a piano string produces a note an octave higher.

Top right: the diatonic scale can be built by means of an interlinked group of triads, producing a succession of 8 notes per octave according to intervallic patterns shown in table (bottom right).

Left: a late 15th century picture by Hans Memling, showing angels playing instruments. Religion has greatly influenced the growth of musical notation and scales.

OSBORNE/MARKS

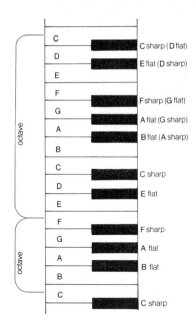

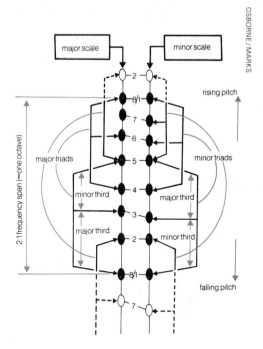

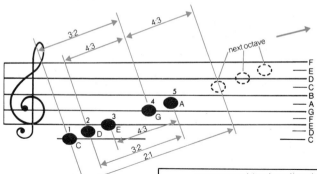

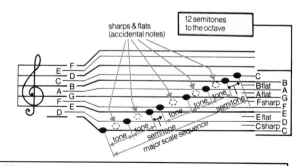

Centre : common pentatonic (five note) scale as it would appear on modern stave when starting from middle C. Notes are related by simple frequency ratios (2 : 1, 3 : 2, 4 : 3).

Centre right : conventional stave (left) distorts true interval relationships between notes. Here, the stave has been expanded to represent actual frequency spacings, leaving gaps for the five 'accidental' notes (not normally granted positions of their own) thus providing the full chromatic scale of 13 notes.

Bottom right : table of common intervals used in scale building.

some common intervals used in scale building		(descending order→increasing frequency)			
			western scale positions		
musical name	musical character	frequency ratio referred to starting note	major	minor	chromatic
unison	consonant	1:1	1	1	1
chromatic semitone	dissonant	25:24 or 19:18	–	–	2
minor-second (diatonic semitone)	dissonant	16:15	–	–	2
lesser whole-tone (minor-tone)	semi-dissonant	10:9	–	–	3
major-second (larger whole-tone)	semi-dissonant	9:8	2	2	3
minor-third	semi-consonant	6:5	–	3	4
major-third	consonant	5:4	3	–	5
perfect–fourth	consonant	4:3	4	4	6
augmented-fourth (diminished-fifth)	semi-consonant	7:5 or 10:7	–	–	7
perfect-fifth	consonant	3:2	5	5	8
minor-sixth	semi-consonant	8:5	–	6	9
major-sixth	consonant	5:3	6	–	10
minor-seventh	semi-consonant	7:4 or 9:5	–	7	11
major-seventh	dissonant	15:8	7	–	12
octave	consonant	2:1	8	8	13

Diatonic scales The apparently unsophisticated pentatonic scale contains not only this collection of fourths, fifths and whole-tones, but also a number of steps between other pairs of notes equivalent to further simple frequency ratios. Important among these are the consonances known as *major-third* and *major-sixth*, and also their semi-consonant *minor* versions. But these more subtle intervals are only approximated within the pentatone, whose whole-tone steps have to be adjusted slightly, or *tempered*, to give true thirds and sixths. From such adjustments, and because of the expressive needs of an evolving music, our present major and minor eight-note scales gradually emerged as modified versions of the most popular ancient modes.

Just as the fifth followed by a fourth to make an octave was basic to ancient scale building, giving three notes with a simple 2:3:4 frequency relationship, so an upward step of a major-third followed by a minor-third to equal a fifth ($\frac{5}{4} \times \frac{6}{5} = \frac{3}{2}$) became an additional vital grouping in modern scales. This set of three notes has a 4:5:6 frequency relationship and is known as a *major triad* (a triad is a group of three notes), paralleled by the *minor triad* in which the middle note is moved down (flattened) to make the first step into a minor-third (10:12:15 pattern). Interlocking groups of such triads provide a complete framework for the two main *diatonic scales*, though there are several alternative endings to the minor scale (diatonic means ranging through the eight conventional tones).

The various consonant and semi-consonant intervals listed in the table appear in these scales not only between the starting note and named note, and within the triadic groupings, but also at other positions whenever several smaller intervals add together appropriately. Thus when all the steps in the major scale are set exactly to give 'just intonation' there are 13 consonances and 4 semi-consonances within the octave. Our feeling for the key or *tonic* note in major-scale melodies is due in some way to this interleaved consonant pattern, an effect less marked with the minor scale and largely lost if too many

extra steps are added—as in *atonal* or 'serial' music. Also, it is because so many of the intervals used in diatonic music have these small-number frequency ratios that BRASS INSTRUMENTS are able to employ selections of *harmonics* (simple multiples of a basic note) to make up their scales.

Tones and semitones Turning to the smaller intervals, it will be seen from the major and minor diatonic scales that the two scales employ seven differently mixed steps of two sizes between adjacent notes. The larger step is the familiar whole-tone and the smaller one a *semitone*—of approximately half the size. If a whole-tone is labelled 'T' and a semitone 'S', the sequence of intervals in a major scale is TTSTTTS, which is obtained by playing the white keys on a piano upwards from the note C. Because Western musical instruments and notation happened to evolve with C-major as the dominant scale, the above pattern can only be repeated from other starting points by adding further notes to divide the whole-tone intervals into semitones where needed. As latecomers, these *accidentals* are known either as sharpened versions of the note below or as flattenings of the note above, and have no true positions of their own on the keyboard or stave. If the stave is redrawn to represent the *real* note spacings the eight plain-letter notes from C to C are now seen to follow the TTSTTTS pattern. It happens that the basic minor-scale scheme (TSTTSTT) can also be played on a keyboard instrument (or drawn on a conventional stave) without using sharps or flats by starting from A, but any other tonic note again demands accidentals for construction of the correct scale sequence.

Chromatic scale As Western music progressed there was an increasing need to shift between major and minor modes and from key to key, and to add extra notes for colour and 'tension', so that all five sharps and flats eventually came into general use, giving a total of 12 semitone steps (13 notes) within each octave. With freely intoned instruments such as the human voice or violin this presents no problems, but devices with fixed tuning—particularly keyboard instruments—raise difficulties because of minor arithmetical irregularities in the 'just' diatonic scales. In order to achieve its correct overall structure, the major scale actually incorporates two slightly different sizes of whole-tone between its individual notes: Pythagoras' original step of 9:8 and a smaller one of 10:9. In addition, the diatonic semitones are joined by two rather smaller steps when *chromatic* notes (extras outside the immediate scheme) are added by splitting the whole-tones. Thus no one size of whole-tone or semitone is correct for filling in the extra five notes, while the addition of such notes creates errors in the existing spacings when these are used as steps in fresh scales.

Various early attempts to deal with this problem led, by the 18th century, to a system of tuning known as *equal temperament*, in which all notes are spaced by the same size of semitone—equivalent in mathematical terms to the twelfth root of two, which is just under 6% of frequency. The regular pattern of frets on a GUITAR is a good visual example of this. Equitempered tuning introduces some minor errors which are a matter for continued dispute, though in the worst case the deviation from 'just' intonation is only just over 1%.

In music-making not dominated by keyboard or other rigidly tuned instruments, the intervals adopted tend to be those found in the 'just' scales. But however the notes may be tempered, the modern chromatic scale of 12 steps per octave may be used—starting at any note—for building any scale made up from semitone or whole-tone units: diatonic major and minor, pentatonic, whole-tone, 12-tone 'serial', and so on.

Above: part of the so-called Antiphonarium which is said to be the oldest musical manuscript in existence. Belonging to the monastery of St Gall, it dates from AD 790 and is the earliest scale notation known. The symbols are called 'neums' and indicate relative pitch.

MUYBRIDGE, Eadweard (1830–1904)

Edward James Muggeridge, the son of a corn merchant, was born in Kingston-upon-Thames, Surrey, England, but emigrated to the United States as a young man of 22 and changed his name to Eadweard Muybridge to make it more Anglo-Saxon. He later became a professional photographer and worked with the famous topographical photographer Carleton A Watkins in San Francisco. Muybridge took hundreds of views of Yosemite and the Pacific coast and these were seen by millionaire Leland Stanford, a former Governor of California, which led to Muybridge becoming one of the first to make satisfactory photographic analyses of motion, and the first to show his results on some form of projector.

Etienne MAREY's pictures of moving horses were known to Stanford and he wanted to prove for himself that a galloping horse's hooves all left the ground when its legs were bunched under its body, not when stretched out. Most authorities say that Stanford had a $5000 bet with fellow horse-owner Frederick MacCrellish, but there is no positive evidence for this. He asked Muybridge, now making a photographic survey of the Pacific coast for the US government, to photograph his favourite trotter, Occident, at full gallop (about 25 mph; 40 km/h) on the Sacramento race course. In May 1872, Muybridge got his first reasonably successful silhouette.

The experiments were interrupted by scandal (Muybridge was accused, but acquitted, of murdering his wife's lover) and he left the USA to take up photographic assignments elsewhere. He returned to California and Stanford's Palo Alto stud farm in 1877. He found that a white background made shorter exposures—perhaps only a thousandth of a second—and slightly clearer silhouettes possible. These at least proved that the horses did lift all four feet off the ground as predicted. Muybridge correctly deduced that this gait was common to all four-footed animals. But he and Stanford were not satisfied. More money was spent (over the years, Stanford is said to have paid out $40,000) and a huge apparatus was constructed, with

a rubber track to avoid dust being raised. Alongside ran a fence 50 feet (15 m) long, marked with vertical lines every 21 inches (53 cm). Opposite this was a row of 12 cameras, also at 21 inch (53 cm) intervals, set off by electromagnets. Later, Muybridge doubled the number of cameras, placing them one foot (30 cm) apart; they were actuated by trip threads under the horses' hooves.

Muybridge published and copyrighted his successful results in 1878 and went on to issue photographs of many animals. He toured America and Europe, addressing learned societies and demonstrating his invention, the *Zoopraxiscope*. In this, successive images were mounted around the edge of a revolving glass disc like that used by Marey. Until EDISON's *Kinetoscope*, 12 years later, this was the most successful machine for reconstituting the movement captured by the original photographs. At the University of Pennsylvania, which seemed ready to meet the vast bills for his experiments, Muybridge used the newly-introduced dry photographic plates to take many more pictures, including some of wild animals. His book *Animal Locomotion* (1887) included 20,000 of them. Three years before he died, Muybridge returned to Kingston, bequeathing to its public library his Zoopraxiscope, many photographs and lantern slides, and his press-cuttings books.

Right: a portrait of Eadweard Muybridge, who is renowned for his photographic analyses of animal and human motion.

Below: front and side views of a movement photographed by Muybridge. The stills of each part of the action were mounted around the edge of a revolving glass disc to create the illusion of movement.

MARY EVANS PICTURE LIBRARY

RADIO TIMES HULTON PICTURE LIBRARY

JACKSON DAY DESIGNS

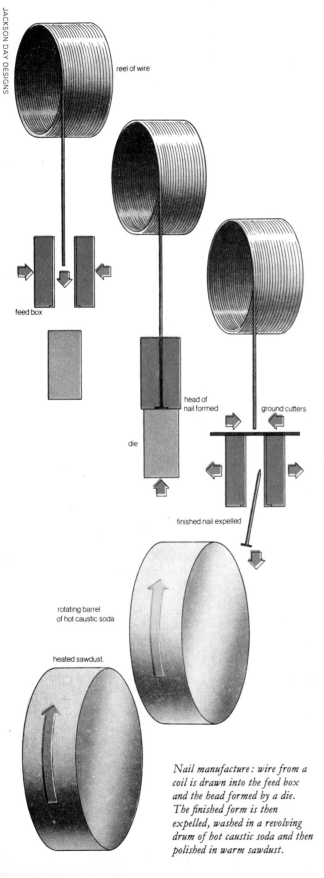

reel of wire

feed box

die

head of
nail formed

ground cutters

finished nail expelled

rotating barrel
of hot caustic soda

heated sawdust.

*Nail manufacture: wire from a
coil is drawn into the feed box
and the head formed by a die.
The finished form is then
expelled, washed in a revolving
drum of hot caustic soda and then
polished in warm sawdust.*

NAIL manufacture

Nail manufacture is one of the most efficient and highly automated of industrial processes. Originally nails were forged by hand; then they were cut from sheets of rolled iron. Mass production came in the nineteenth century, when a method of producing nails on automatic machines from coils of wire was developed. The basic principle of the nail forming machine has not changed since then.

Wire is drawn from a coil into the machine. The head is formed by flattening the end of the wire against a die; then the wire is pinched and cut to the correct length by ground cutters moving together simultaneously to form the point. Finally, the expelling mechanism knocks the finished nail into a pan at the bottom of the machine. The basic operation is augmented by additional forming or twisting devices for special nails, such as roofing nails with twisted shanks and those with helical spirals to give an extra-firm grip.

After forming, nails can go through a variety of treatments, depending on the intended use. They are cleaned in a rotating barrel of hot caustic soda to remove grease and wire 'nippings'. Then they are often tumbled in a second revolving drum containing heated sawdust to give them a bright finish. Other finishes often applied to nails include GALVANIZING, cement-coating and *sherardizing*, a process of applying a corrosion-resistant coating of zinc by heating the object to a temperature of about 300°C (570°F) in a closed container with a powder of zinc dust and zinc oxide.

The largest nail factory in Britain is at Cardiff; it contains more than 200 fully automatic nail forming machines, from those weighing only a few hundred pounds to giant machines weighing seven tons. The total production of the machines is about 1400 nails a second, or about 300 million in a normal week. This is about 800 tons by weight, or about half the total production of the country.

The PACKAGING MACHINERY in a nail factory is also highly automated. It includes magnetic elevators which convey the nails to weighing machines, where they are dropped into cartons past magnetic poles which automatically stack them in parallel rows. After packing the nails are demagnetized.

*Right: an illustration from Diderot's Encyclopedia of 1784
showing the forge where nails were handmade and a selection of
nails. The nails with square heads in the top row left were
probably horseshoe nails; some of the long ones have shaped heads for
decorative purposes, or for retaining roof tiles, for example.*

*Below: right: modern nail making machinery at Cardiff, Wales.
Wire is drawn from a reel and flattened on the end; the cut-off
and formation of the point are the same operation. The factory
has 200 machines averaging seven nails a second.*

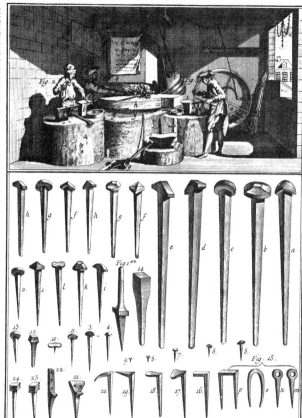

MARY EVANS PICTURE LIBRARY

GKN (SOUTH WALES) LTD

NASMYTH, James (1808–1890)

James Nasmyth, renowned in his own time as the inventor of the steam hammer which was crucial to the growth of railways and iron ships, did not patent his invention until he had already seen it realized by others. This was, however, only one of many innovations which he made in MACHINE TOOL manufacture.

Nasmyth had a fortunate childhood; his father Alexander was a landscape painter in Edinburgh, whose house was frequented by scientists and artists. Among James's boyhood friends were the sons of an ironmaster and a colour manufacturer who let him learn chemistry and mechanics by watching the processes they employed. This stimulus served him far better than his formal schooling, which ended at the age of 12, although he continued to attend classes at the Edinburgh School of Arts and University. Meantime he had set up a little brass foundry—in his bedroom. There, and in his father's workshop, he made model steam engines which were good enough to pay for his studies, and to win him a post, when he was 21, as assistant, in the Lambeth engine works, to Henry MAUDSLAY. Even before his move south, he had designed a steam carriage and a mode of chain traction whereby steam could be used to haul canal barges.

In London James Nasmyth had not been with Maudslay long before he had designed a flexible wire shaft for a drill, and a circular mechanical file to produce hexagonal nuts of uniform size. Nasmyth learned much from his two years with Maudslay and, after his master's death in 1831, decided to set up in business on his own as an engine and machine tool maker, first near his native Edinburgh, next in Manchester, and then at Patricroft, where he established his Bridgewater Foundry in 1836, when not yet 28. Two years later he met Ann Hartop while on a visit to the Barnsley iron foundry where her father was manager. According to his account he fell in love and proposed within two days, although they were not married until 1840.

Nasmyth's move to Lancashire coincided with the railway boom, of which he was quick to take advantage. Now he added to the increasing repertoire of lathes, drills and boring and planing machines, devices for cutting key-ways, centring rods before turning on a lathe, and a shaping machine nicknamed the 'steam arm' because the tool-holder was drawn to and fro by crank and connecting rod, rather like a horizontal steam engine. The steam arm was intended for planing the smaller parts of locomotives, as he had contracted to build 20 for the Great Western Railway.

In 1839, their engineer asked for his advice on how to forge a paddle shaft for the 'Great Britain', because there was not a forge hammer which was powerful enough for such an undertaking. Nasmyth decided that the problem lay in having the hammer fall through an acute angle on the work (if the object to be forged was too large the hammer suffered still worse from 'want of compass, of range and fall') nor could it be made too heavy, or it would snap its helve. He conceived of a hammer held in guides directly above the work, rather like a PILEDRIVER (or a guillotine), raised by steam. At first it was allowed to drop by gravity, but soon was modified so as to be double-acting. But Nasmyth did no more than sketch out his ideas in his *Scheme Book*, and it was only after seeing one at Le Creusot two years later that he decided to patent it. It was an immediate success, forging all the heavy wrought iron members needed in marine engineering, such as shafts, plates and anchors, and in locomotive building. When equipped with a die, the hammer could also be used to impart a given shape.

In 1845, Nasmyth adapted the same principle for a steam powered piledriver; and also based an inverted steam engine on similar geometry. Highly honoured and immensely successful, at the height of his career, Nasmyth resolved to retire at 48. He bought a cottage at Penshurst, Kent and spent the next 30 years as an astronomer, developing a number of fruitful theories on the surfaces of Sun and Moon, which he sought to demonstrate experimentally, becoming an authority on the Moon.

Nasmyth's autobiography suggests that he always had a yearning for the romantic and the antique; he produced drawings of his Gothic fantasies, and lamented that technical progress, to which he had contributed so much, was ruining beautiful old towns. But although a good businessman, his chief inventions were those of an artist interested in geometrical simplification—his joy in them seems almost aesthetic.

Below: Nasmyth standing at the controls of his steam hammer at Bridgewater Foundry, Patricroft. The steam cylinder is at the top of the heavy iron frame; below it is the ram linking the piston to the huge hammer block running in guides on the frame.

Right: Nasmyth was the son of a painter, and this picture is his own work.

THE SCIENCE MUSEUM

CITY OF SALFORD CULTURAL SERVICES

NAVIGATION

Navigation is a business of motion. The Polynesians learnt to steer their catamarans by the stars and by the motion of the Pacific swells. The Mediterranean seaman tended to rely on prevailing winds until, around 1200, the magnetic COMPASS appeared. It was soon found that the direction indicated was not true north but varied over the Earth, this *variation* now being printed on charts. When iron and steel ships were built, compensation for the consequent deviation became necessary, a problem solved in the last hundred years by the GYROCOMPASS, which measures the direction of the Earth's axis without using magnetism.

In the Middle Ages, the navigator would cast over the stern a log tied to a knotted line which he would pay out, counting the knots while a half minute sand-glass ran dry. Modern logs take the form of propellers or use water pressure, the latest types employing electronic principles. However, the word knot, meaning a *nautical mile per hour*, is also retained. The nautical mile is 6080 feet (1852 m), almost exactly a minute (one sixtieth of a degree) of latitude.

Position finding from course, or direction of travel, and from speed, according to the time since leaving a starting point, is known as *dead reckoning* or DR. Were there neither tides nor winds the navigator at sea could rely on DR but, in practice, *fixing* or finding position by other means is necessary at intervals. On land, it is possible to pin-point a position on a map but at sea it is a matter of using distant objects, for example taking *bearings* on landmarks ashore. At night, these directions may be taken, with the aid of a compass, on a LIGHTHOUSE.

In the wind oceans, dead reckoning checks have traditionally depended on astro-navigation. Each point on the Earth's surface has a unique vertical and therefore a unique horizontal. The navigator measures the *altitude* or angle above the horizon of Sun, Moon or star by means of his SEXTANT. According to where he thinks he is, he then calculates what the angle ought to be at the time. If the sextant altitude is greater than the calculated value the correction will be towards the star, the distance in nautical miles being the difference of altitude in minutes. A second star's altitude and a second correction will fix position.

Although astro-navigation is a worldwide aid, it is not 'all weather'. Cloud may cover the sky and fog will blot out the horizon which, in any event, may not be visible at all during the night so that star observations may have to be restricted to dusk and dawn.

Electronics at sea   In the early 1900s, MARCONI successfully demonstrated radio communication which was used initially to broadcast time signals for checking the chronometers (accurate clocks) carried on ships for astro-navigation. It was soon found that an aerial [antenna] wound in a loop could detect the direction from which a radio wave was coming. The navigator now had eyes which could 'see' a radio beacon at night or in fog.

By squeaking and timing the echoes, bats have learnt to fly inside pitch black caves. Radio waves travel nearly a million times as fast as sound waves, seven times round the Earth in a second. Nevertheless, shortly before World War 2, echoes were being measured by radio. Using a directional aerial, generally in the form of a dish, distances and directions could be found and the results displayed on the face of a CATHODE RAY TUBE. Thus radar enabled the mariner to see coastlines and other ships at night or in fog.

In recent decades, more money and effort has been expended

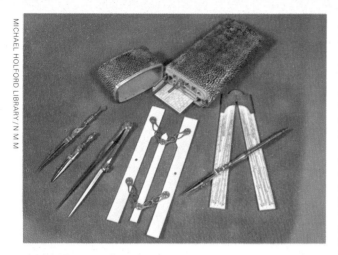

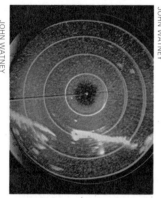

Top: these navigational instruments, very little different from those used today, were owned by Captain Cook. The dividers are for measuring the distances on charts, while the parallel rulers enable lines to be drawn in a particular direction from any point, parallel to the compass rose marked on charts.

Centre left: today, even comparatively small craft may be equipped with radar. The coastline, some inland features, and other craft show up as blips on the screen. Centre right: micro-electronics have made possible this hand held radio locator. It can be tuned to a coastal radio beacon, and oriented to give the weakest or no signal. The beacon's bearing is then read off. Two such bearings, selected with the aid of an almanac, give a fix on the chart (lower picture).

on marine aids than in all the previous history of man. The lead line has been replaced by the *echo sounder* (see ASDIC AND SONAR), which times the travel of sound waves from the hull of a ship to the seabed and back.

During World War 2 the *Loran* and *Decca Navigator* systems came into use. These set up patterns over the earth comparable to the intersecting ripples of water when stones are thrown simultaneously into a pond. More recently, *Omega*, an ultra long range very low frequency system has been developed.

All these systems work on the same principle, though there are practical differences between them. If two radio transmitters send out the same signal, say a continuous tone, the two WAVE MOTIONS will coincide with each other—that is, they will be in phase—along certain lines. These lines form a hyperbolic pattern around the transmitters. A ship picking up the signals exactly in phase must therefore be on one of these lines, which are marked on charts. To give a precise fix, signals from another pair of stations must be compared, the hyperbolic lines from which are also marked. Combining the two gives a unique position, once the lines involved are known.

This is the principle of the Decca system, which uses additional lane identification signals transmitted from the ground stations every minute to give a unique fix. These drive automatic counters on board the ship, so that a continuous readout of position is displayed.

The basic Loran system uses pulses instead of continuous wave transmissions, giving rather less information but a greater accuracy at long distances; the Loran C system combines both. These systems are also used by aircraft. A limited system called Consol, giving direction details only, is used by yachtsmen.

The most recent system involves the use of SATELLITES which orbit the Earth, broadcasting details of their orbits by means of a signal code which is changed by remote control from the ground as the orbit alters. As the satellite moves across the sky, the rate of change of its DOPPLER shift varies—its distance from the ship varies most rapidly when it is close to the horizon, and least when it is overhead. The orbit and Doppler information are fed into a COMPUTER on board the ship, which calculates the ship's position to great accuracy.

Air navigation At about the same time that MARCONI was developing radio, the WRIGHT brothers flew the first man-carrying heavier than air machine. The seamen who tried to navigate these early machines soon discovered the special difficulties. A ship can 'heave to', but an aircraft must fly on, gulping down the fuel it needs to keep it aloft. Also, at these speeds, there is little time for navigating.

Before take-off, the pilot prepares a complete dead reckoning picture of his journey known as a *flight plan* which he amends as he progresses on his way. Originally, course and speed could only be found relative to the air which itself travels with the wind. Nowadays, radio Doppler (see AVIONICS) can measure speed over the ground and simple computers can translate the results into position.

In the air, the pilot needs aids that tell him not where he is but what to do. In the early days, the loop aerial was simply pointed at a beacon on the destination airfield and the aeroplane lined up with the loop. Alternatively crude beams of radio waves produced by ground stations might be used. Such aids were vulnerable to bad weather and, after World War 2 high frequency directional beacons known as *VOR* and a distance measuring equipment, *DME*, became the standard aids. Loran and Decca are not as much use because they find positions rather than point the way.

In place of astro, the aeroplane may be fitted with an INERTIAL GUIDANCE SYSTEM consisting of a platform carrying accelerometers that measure the unique vertical with gyroscopes that 'remember' the sky, and a computer that gives position continuously. These systems are expensive; only large fast commercial airliners or small military aircraft, where expense is no bar, can afford to be fitted. Even these precision gyroscopes tend to drift 1° of angle per hour so that positional errors are about one nautical mile for each hour of flight.

An aircraft is much more difficult to control than a ship for, unless kept level, it will not fly straight. The human ear carries balancers but, at high speeds, the accelerations distort their messages. Hence early pilots restricted their flying to within view of the ground.

At night, or in cloud, INSTRUMENTS are essential but the load on the pilot is severe. Forty years ago, *automatic pilots* were being developed and are now standard fitment except in light aircraft. The autopilot, combined with ILS, a precision radio beam, and a radio ALTIMETER to measure clearance above the runway, have made automatic landing in fog possible. Indeed 'push button' flights are now made, the pilot hardly touching the control column. All the aids mentioned may be linked to the autopilot through a computer.

Efforts to make air navigation safer have led to the introduction of 'redundancy' whereby three or more systems operate simultaneously in an aircraft so that, if one disagrees with the other two, it can be disconnected as faulty. For automatic landing, triplicate or quadruplicate autopilots, ILS receivers and radio altimeters are fitted; in high subsonic or supersonic aircraft, three inertial navigators may be provided if the

The navigation desk of the frigate HMS Charybdis (above) is similar to the yachtsman's except for the Decca Navigator above the table. This gives readings which can be plotted directly on an overprinted chart, as shown below on a small scale. There are three dials; two readings are sufficient for an accurate fix. Decca operates in Europe and other major traffic areas; Charybdis and other ocean-going vessels also carry Loran for longer range use.
Below right: navigation by dead reckoning. This schematic view—the details are not to scale—shows a vessel taking the calculated course for about four hours, then taking a fix on two objects. This fix shows it to be at '02.04 fix' rather than at the dead-reckoned DR point. 11 minutes are allowed for working out a new course.

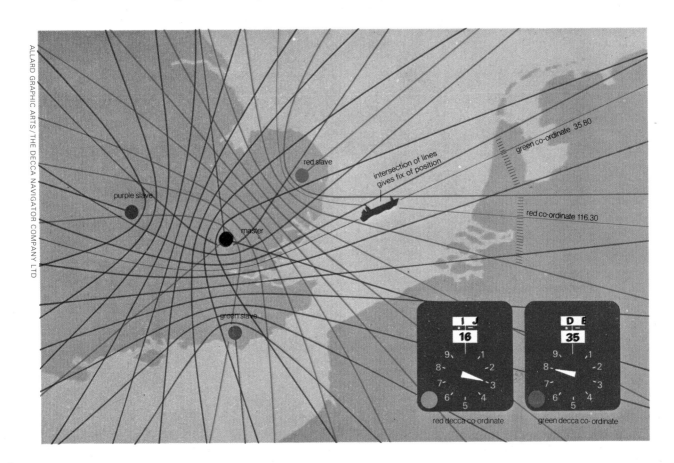

red slave

purple slave

master

green slave

intersection of lines gives fix of position

green co-ordinate 35.80

red co-ordinate 116.30

red decca co-ordinate

green decca co-ordinate

verticals that they measure are used to level the aircraft.

The aids employed by airmen have not greatly affected marine navigation. VOR and DME have insufficient range and the time taken for a sea voyage is too long for inertial navigation, except for naval submarines, to which extremely complex systems may be fitted. *Autohelmsmen* are however, being provided to many ships and computers are used in large vessels.

Collision

A collision at sea does not always involve loss of life. On the other hand, aircraft are fragile structures travelling twenty times as fast and collisions are generally disastrous. Aircraft are smaller than ships and very difficult to see.

Air collision avoidance has therefore been made the responsibility of AIR TRAFFIC CONTROL, a system that lays down routes and timings along aerial routes known as *airways* and adjusts their paths to ensure safe separation. A controller covers a certain area and therefore the flight plans of aircraft passing through are cut into *flight strips* which may be assembled on a board so that progress can be followed. To assist the controller in his decisions, digital computers are increasingly being used.

Aircraft are separated vertically as well as horizontally and, for this purpose, the BAROMETER-type altimeter is used. To help the controller, aircraft now automatically signal altitude when picked up by a ground controller's radar.

Recent increases in shipping traffic has led to the introduction of 'one way' lanes at sea, for example, in the Strait of Dover, and port control systems using radar to watch vessels are now coming into use. In open waters, however, ship-borne radar is still the main collision avoidance aid whereas the civil pilot uses radar to detect the storm areas ahead by picking up 'echoes' from the large water drops.

Space navigation

Journeys into space are based on very thorough 'flight planning' so that a Moon landing or a splashdown may be predicted with extraordinary precision many days or even months in advance. This is possible because there are no winds or tides and the gravitational fields of Sun, planets and moons are known very exactly, so that the 'dead reckoning' can be remarkably precise.

For launch, inertial navigation is used but, once in space, the craft and its crew are weightless and there is no unique vertical. Although position cannot be established, the platform is essential in order to keep the spacecraft on a steady alignment, which is set according to the brighter stars, while the motors are fired to change the velocity and amend the orbit. The accelerometers then measure the change of velocity and, when the correct value is reached, the thrust is cut off automatically.

Astro-navigation on Earth only works because the navigator needs just to fix his position relative to the Earth's surface. In space, there is no such reference and the stars can only give orientation in two dimensions. The third dimension of position in space is established by radar from the Earth supported by computing, though a modified form of astro-navigation can be used close to a planet or a moon where a reference surface exists. Doppler from the Earth measures velocity with extraordinary accuracy but the spacecraft is also fitted with Doppler navigation aids for landing purposes. Indeed, its on-board computing makes possible a safe return to Earth should the radio links break down.

NEON LIGHT (see discharge tube)

NEUTRINO (see particle physics)

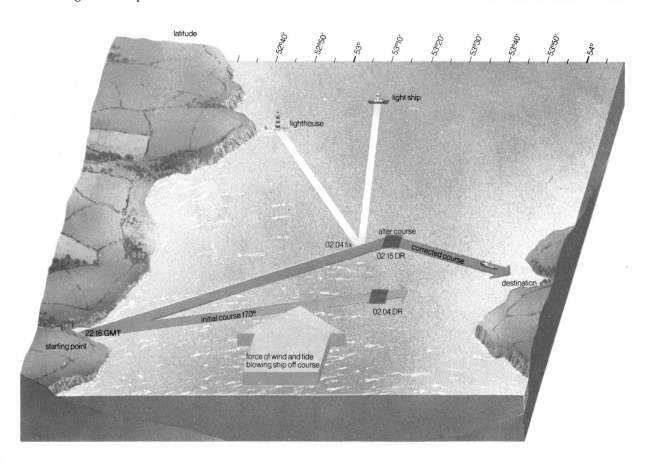

latitude · 52°40' · 52°50' · 53° · 53°10' · 53°20' · 53°30' · 53°40' · 53°50' · 54°

light ship

lighthouse

alter course

02.04 fix

02.15 DR

corrected course

destination

initial course 170°

02.04 DR

22.16 GMT

starting point

force of wind and tide blowing ship off course

NEUTRON

The neutron is one of the types of particle inhabiting the NUCLEUS of the ATOM. It is almost identical in its properties to the other inhabitant, the PROTON, except that it carries no electric charge.

It was discovered by Chadwick in 1932 when he watched charged particles, flying out from a radioactive source, hitting targets such as a thin layer of paraffin wax. Beyond the target he had a detector which told him that something was coming out, but this 'something' had not the characteristics of the well known proton or GAMMA RAY. He was able to deduce that it was a neutral twin of the proton which was being knocked out of the target nucleus. It was given the name neutron and its mass was calculated as about two million million million millionths of a gramme, which is almost identical to that of the proton and two thousand times that of the ELECTRON.

This discovery removed a puzzle in the observed masses of the chemical ELEMENTS. When only the proton and electron were known, it was not understood why the masses of all the elements were not multiples of the simplest element, hydrogen, which has one proton in its nucleus and one electron in orbit around it. The existence of the neutrons, added in various numbers to the protons, explains the big variations in atomic mass. The number of neutrons in a nucleus is generally close to the number of protons though the heavier the element the more 'extra' neutrons are found. One element may have several types of nuclei, ISOTOPES, with different numbers of neutrons.

The neutron is a comparatively stable particle. Left to itself, it exists for about twelve minutes before breaking up (or 'decaying') into a proton, an electron and another neutral particle without mass called a *neutrino* (see PARTICLE PHYSICS). This decay can also take place when the neutron is locked in a nucleus. The protons then tend to remain in place (changing the chemical element type of the nucleus) while the electrons and neutrinos fly out. It is known as *beta decay* of the nucleus and the emerging electrons are the *beta rays* which were seen by the first investigators of RADIOACTIVITY earlier this century.

Neutrons play a vital part in the operation of NUCLEAR REACTORS and A-BOMBS. It is by sending an additional neutron into a heavy nucleus that it can be induced to FISSION, breaking up into lighter nuclei with the release of energy. The neutrons flying around in reactors are also used to produce isotopes for use in research, in agriculture, in medicine and in industry. Another more recent practical application is the use of neutron beams in radiotherapy, replacing the more familiar X-RAYS, to break up cancerous cells.

One of the more unusual objects yet detected in the universe is the *neutron star*, which is formed of an extremely dense material whose structure is not yet fully understood. Typically a neutron star has a radius of only 10 km (6.2 miles) and yet is more than a million times more massive than the Earth. *Pulsars* (see ASTROPHYSICS) are thought to be rotating neutron stars.

Right: apparatus for neutron activation analysis. A fast neutron generator is situated in a well (bottom) which is filled with polyethylene powder. A disc-shaped sample of the material to be analyzed is passed down the metal tube to the generator where it is bombarded with neutrons. The sample is then returned to the analyzer and its radioactivity is measured with a gamma ray detector (right) shielded with lead bricks. The composition of the sample can be determined very accurately using this technique, and it is not normally necessary to process the sample chemically.

NEWCOMEN SOCIETY/PHOTOS: ALEC LUMSDEN

NEWCOMEN, Thomas (c1663–1729)

The first practical steam engine was invented, not by James WATT, but by an obscure ironmonger from Devon, Thomas Newcomen, who built his first steam engine over half a century before Watt's improved version. Despite research in recent years little is known about Newcomen: no portrait of him exists, even his date of birth is uncertain, but we do know he was christened in Dartmouth on 24 February 1663. His father was a merchant and the family were Nonconformists. Young Thomas probably served an apprenticeship in Exeter; then in about 1685 he set up as an ironmonger in Dartmouth with a partner called John Calley. When he was 42 Newcomen married his wife Hannah and their new house became a meeting place for local Baptists, including his partner Calley.

Very little information survives about Newcomen's early experiments or how much he knew of other people's experiments. In France during 1690 Denis PAPIN had built a small model to show that steam could move a piston inside a cylinder —the basis of a steam engine. A few years later Captain Thomas Savery demonstrated a steam-powered pump to the Royal Society. This was partially successful, but it was not a true steam engine because it did not have a reciprocating piston. Savery's patent of 1698, which covered the ATMOSPHERIC ENGINE was, however, a great handicap to Newcomen's developments and in 1705 Newcomen and Calley entered into partnership with Savery.

The first steam engine was built in 1712. Newcomen had visited the tin mines of Devon and Cornwall in the course of business and realized that there was a need for a source of power to pump water out of the deep mines. They could not find a customer for their steam engine near Dartmouth but their Baptist friends with coal mines in the Midlands needed pumps —and they had plenty of cheap coal with which to fire a boiler. The actual location of this first engine is a mystery but it was probably near Dudley Castle in Worcestershire. A drawing of the engine survives and, from the size of a man stoking the boiler, it was large and impressive.

Newcomen placed the large vertical cylinder above a domed boiler. Inside the cylinder, a piston moved up and down and this was connected by a chain to a see-saw beam mounted high in the engine house. At the other end of the see-saw, rods were attached and these descended to the water pump in the mine. The pump side of the see-saw was the heavier, and consequently it rested in the down position. A coal fire under the boiler heated the water and produced steam which was fed into the cylinder below the piston. The steam was condensed by a spray of cold water and this created a partial vacuum. The atmospheric pressure acting on the upper side of the piston forced it downwards. At the end of the stroke, the heavy pump rods which had been raised by the see-saw moved down again thus driving the water pump.

Newcomen's atmospheric steam engines, or fire engines as they were often called, became widely used not only in Britain, but also throughout Europe. Unfortunately because of the patent restrictions Newcomen did not gain full credit for his work nor did he become rich. He died while staying in London at the age of 66, almost unknown.

Left : two views of the only Newcomen engine surviving in unaltered form and working order. Originally erected at Griff, near Nuneaton, it is now at Dartmouth. The top picture shows the chain connecting the beam to the pump; below is the massive 22 inch (56 cm) diameter cylinder at the other end of the beam.

NEWSPAPER PRODUCTION

Newspapers began as pamphlets and broadsheets in the 17th century. Their original function was the dissemination of news and opinion, but advertisers quickly found them useful. Technical developments in the Industrial Revolution and the growth of the popular press in the 19th century have resulted in the production of newspapers as we know them today, using techniques which had not changed for many years until the present development of electronic newspaper production.

Advertising   Newspaper advertising is in two categories: *classified* and *display*. Classified adverts appear under special categories and are usually printed in a self-contained section; display adverts are intermixed throughout the paper with editorial content. The number of pages in a newspaper is based on a predetermined ratio of advertising to editorial matter. Since the advertising layout can be determined well in advance of the news, a plan of each page showing the advertising layout is given to the editorial department to assist in the layout of the paper.

Classified advertising is sold over the telephone; display advertising is obtained by salesmen in the field, supported by an art department which can prepare artwork as necessary. Advertising is indispensable in modern newspapers because the production costs of the paper could never be met by newspaper circulation alone.

Editorial   The gathering, selection and editing of the news, as well as the writing of leaders [editorials] carrying the commentary, is the function of the editorial department. Some newspapers keep the straight reporting of the news separate from the editorial comment, and some newspapers allow the news stories to be written according to the editorial opinion.

In the latter case the story will often carry a *by-line* (the reporter's name).

The Editor usually has a conference each day with his aides to determine the relative importance of the news coming in; a rough plan is made and kept under review as the news breaks. The news comes in from a variety of sources, including local reporters in the field, often working on special assignments such as sports or financial news, and international news agency wire services. Local news often goes directly to the *news desk*, while international news goes to *sub-editors*.

The British sub-editor is called the *desk-man* or *copy-reader* in the USA. His job is to help select material according to its importance, since far more news comes into the news room each day than can be printed in the paper. The British sub-editor often rewrites a story, condensing it to save space; his north American counterpart will more likely write in background information, so that the reader seeing a developing story can catch up on it. An American news story is often written in such a way that the last few paragraphs are short and not so essential, so that they can be cut if necessary for space reasons.

Apart from the mainstream of the news, general articles on a wide range of subjects, often suggested by the news, are prepared by writers in the *feature department*. The taking and selection of pictures is organized by the *picture editor*.

Receipt of news   *Copy* (written news) is typed in the office or received over the telephone by *copytakers* who type stories dictated from all over the country or even abroad by reporters and correspondents. In the *wire room*, or *telegraph room*, a nonstop flow of news and pictures comes in through a worldwide communications network. Teletype machines (see

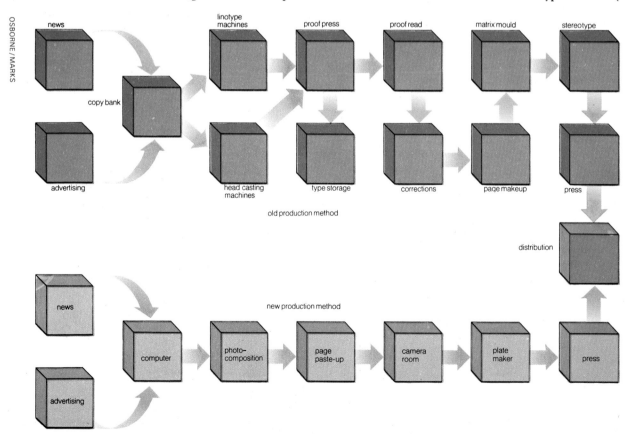

OSBORNE/MARKS

old production method

new production method

THE MANSELL COLLECTION

HARRIS INTERTYPE

YORKSHIRE POST AND EVENING POST LTD

Top: the Hoe Type-Revolving Printing Machine was patented in *1847* and was the first successful rotary machine. It had impression cylinders arranged around a main cylinder which held the type; the speed of the machine was limited only by the speed of the paper feeders. The machine pictured was being used in *1860* to print the Daily Telegraph; it weighed thirty tons and was imported from New York in *47* crates. With ten impression cylinders it could print up to *25,000* impressions an hour.
Above centre: an electronic editing and proofing terminal.
Above: the pressroom at Yorkshire Post Newspapers Ltd.

TELEPRINTER) are operated by keyboards at the other end of the wire, using RADIO links and submarine CABLES between the continents. Pictures are sent out by fitting a photograph to the drum of a transmitting machine. The drum rotates and the shades of black and white in the photograph are converted into electronic impulses of varying intensity which are converted at the receiving end back into a photo by a similar drum holding photo-sensitive paper (see FACSIMILE TRANSMISSION).

The major wire services are Reuters, Associated Press and United Press International. In addition, there are national counterparts such as the Press Association serving Great Britain, and Extel, which supplies sporting and financial news. Many of the largest newspapers also operate their own press service, sending their news and features to subscribing papers.

Production Copy is sent to the *composing room*, where it is set into type. Before 1886, each letter was set by hand in lead. Since then the bulk of lines in the newspaper have been set by the LINOTYPE machine, which is operated by a keyboard. When the operator strikes a key, a brass *matrix* or *mould* for the appropriate letter drops into a slot; the operator inserts space bands and hyphenates words if necessary to *justify* the line (make it the right length), and the machine injects molten lead into the matrices, creating a line of type. (Headlines are usually set on a Ludlow machine, using the same method except that the matrices are assembled by hand.)

Since World War 2, Linotypes have been adapted to be operated by punched tape. Since the late 1950s *computers* have been used to justify lines. Computerized typesetting, called *teletypesetting* or TTS, has tripled the capacity of the Linotype machine so that it can produce ten or fifteen lines a minute.

When the copy is set, a *proof* sheet is printed and sent to the *readers* so that corrections can be made. The corrected type matter is then sent to the *stone*, or page make-up area, where it is carefully fitted into page forms. Photographs are fitted into the page in the form of zinc *half-tone blocks*, prepared by photo-ENGRAVING. The picture is re-photographed through a prism, so that the new negative is a mirror image of the picture, and through a screen which is divided into fine lines. The screen breaks up the light into dots of varying intensity according to the light and dark parts of the photo. (Cartoons and line drawings are exposed without the screen, producing a *line block*.) The negative is placed over a zinc plate which is coated with photo-sensitive chemicals. Brilliant light from arc lamps bakes the coating on where it passes through the negative; elsewhere it remains soluble. The soluble parts are washed away and the plate is *bitten* in a bath of acid.

The assembled page is taken to the *stereotyping* department, where printing plates are made from it. A sheet of papier-mâché-like material called a *flong* is placed over it and subjected to pressure in a moulding press. The resulting mould, also called a *matrix*, is curved, dried and placed in a casting machine, which uses it to make a semicylindrical metal plate which weighs about 40 lb (18 kg) and is a mirror image of the news-paper page. This curved plate is mounted on the *letterpress* which prints the paper. If a newspaper has a large circulation, it may have several presses and several plates will be required; the plate-casting machine has been automated over the years so that it can produce up to seven plates every two minutes.

The rotary LETTERPRESS PRINTING machine may be up to 100 feet (about 30 m) long and weigh 300 tons. Using reels of newsprint weighing a ton and carrying five miles (more than 8 km) of paper, it can print up to 70,000 copies of the paper per hour. The press also cuts and folds the newspapers, and

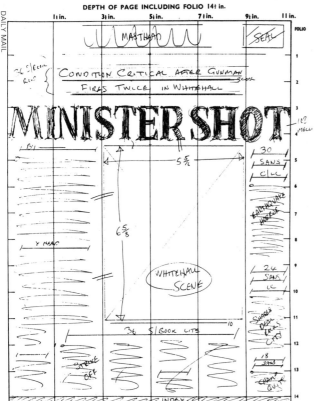

automatic equipment is used to tie them in bundles or put them in plastic bags. Most newspapers distribute their own product, but some larger papers use wholesale distributors who send the papers all over the world.

New methods The letterpress printing technique described above has been used for over half a century without fundamental change; most of the newspapers in the world are still produced that way. Using electronics and computers, changes are now taking place which allow faster production, savings in manpower and other costs, and better reproduction of pictures, especially colour. The key to these changes is the switch to *offset* printing, also called *photo-offset* and LITHOGRAPHY.

In the USA, where developments have been more rapid, more than half of the 1761 daily newspapers have switched to offset printing; the largest newspapers are still printed using the letterpress method because of their investment in presses, which may last for fifty years.

Offset printing begins with a *photocomposition* machine which replaces the Linotype and the entire hot-metal process. For the same price as a Linotype machine, the photocomposition machine can set lines of type ten times as fast. The *make-up* operator assembles a *paste-up* newspaper page, using columns of type produced by the photocomposing machine. (The machine can also mix sizes and styles of type, unlike the Linotype.) The paste-up is then photographed, and the negative is exposed to the *offset plate*, an aluminium plate coated with photosensitive material. This litho plate is not a relief plate but a flat or *planographic* one; the press applies ink and water to the plate; the image area of the plate accepts the ink but rejects the water; and the image is transferred on to a rubber blanket which then transfers it to the paper. Printing plates have been developed which are produced photographically but can be

Daily Mail

THURSDAY, JUNE 14, 1977   3p

WIN A CAR
FORTNIGHT
Page 12

Condition critical after gunman
fires twice in Whitehall

MINISTER SHOT

Daily Mail Reporter

A GOVERNMENT Minister was shot down by a gunman in Whitehall last night.

As two policemen disarmed the attacker a police car rushed the unconscious Minister across Westminster Bridge to St Thomas's Hospital, where his condition was later said to be critical.

Witnesses said two shots were fired by a fair-haired young man dressed in a black shirt and jeans. He was dragged, struggling, to Cannon Row police station and questioned by Special Branch men. He is thought to be an American.

The news was telephoned to the Queen at Balmoral. As a shocked House of Commons was told of the shooting by the Speaker the hospital issued its first bulletin.

Bodyguard

Earthquake hits five more cities

OVER 5,000 people are feared dead in the earthquake which devastated large areas of Northern Chile yesterday.

Share deals halted by City probe

I'll quit, says new champion

Police hold back crowds in Whitehall after last night's shooting.

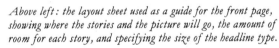

Engineers' strike called off

Arrests

Above left: the layout sheet used as a guide for the front page, showing where the stories and the picture will go, the amount of room for each story, and specifying the size of the headline type.

Above, second from left: the assembled page forme. The justified lines of type, headlines, half-tone blocks and so forth are locked tightly into a frame. The page forme itself could be used to print the newspaper, but would have to be raised and lowered for each impression. It was done that way before the invention of the more efficient rotary press.

Above, third from left: the flong, or matrix, being removed from the page forme. Pressure in a moulding press causes the soft paper-like material of the flong to take the impression of the page forme. The flong, unlike the page forme can be curved.

Below, far left: the semicylindrical metal plate, which is a mirror image of the completed newspaper page, is removed from the casting machine which has cast it using the flong as a mould. The plate weighs about 40 lb (18 kg) and is installed on the press and used to do the actual printing.

Left: installing the reels of paper on the press. The paper is called newsprint and is made of mechanical wood pulp. Spruce is usually used and the method is relatively inexpensive, since it only involves grinding the logs and not cooking the wood with chemicals. The paper has a high content of non-cellulosic matter (which would be removed in cooking) and is not expected to last long. The reel of newsprint is about five miles (8 km) long and weighs about a ton; the press can print 70,000 papers per hour.

Above: the completed front page of the newspaper.

Above and below : two views of the press at the Washington (DC) Evening Star. A letterpress machine, once installed, may last fifty years. Many American papers have switched to photo-offset, but the largest newspapers have a large investment in equipment which cannot be done away with. In cities with more than one newspaper, they sometimes cut costs by sharing the printing plant and the advertising revenue, remaining independent editorially.

used to make a flong, or mounted directly on a letterpress, making possible a combination of the methods.

The development of offset printing has encouraged the greater use of electronics and computers. Photocomposition machines are built which can set 500 lines a minute. The news can be stored on magnetic discs (see DATA STORAGE) and shown on a *video display terminal* (VDT) which uses a CATHODE RAY TUBE similar to a TELEVISION screen. The copy can be reviewed, corrected, and brought up to date while it is still on the computer. When the copy is ready it can be sent by wire or punched tape directly to the photocomposing machine. Other systems use optical CHARACTER RECOGNITION (OCR), in which the typing is done on a special machine whose output can be read by the photocomposer. The new machinery eliminates the need for proofs, retyped corrections and the hot metal process, as well as storing copy in the computer until it is needed, resulting in enormous savings of time and manpower.

Photocomposing machines are being developed which will reproduce entire pages, with photographs and art work, eliminating much of the paste-up work. Laser beams will be used to engrave plates; these will be operated directly from the composing machine, eliminating the need for the camera which now produces the page negative. The printing press itself may some day be replaced by an ELECTROSTATIC process similar to Xerox copying (see XEROGRAPHY).

In the future, the problem of rising cost and scarcity of newsprint, together with distribution of newspapers where transport is difficult, will also be a focus of research and development along with production itself.

NEWTON, Sir Isaac (1642–1727)

On the early morning of Christmas Day 1642, in a Lincolnshire farmhouse, was born the greatest scientific genius the world has known. Isaac Newton was a premature and tiny baby, and the midwives who went off to get medicines for him doubted whether he would be alive on their return. Yet from these undistinguished origins arose the man whose mind laid the foundations of many branches of modern science.

Isaac's father, an illiterate yeoman farmer, had died three months previously. Although the cottage at Woolsthorpe is described as a manor house, and Isaac Newton became in effect lord of the manor, he was not heir to any fortune and he was expected to become a working farmer like his father.

His background did allow him to receive a good schooling in the local day schools and, later, in nearby Grantham. He was by no means an outstanding scholar—he was not very interested in the classical studies of the day, and spent much of his time making working models and studying the world around him. When prompted by his schoolmaster, by such tricks as placing him low in the class, he would make a successful effort to shine at his schoolwork. All his pocket money, however, went on buying tools so that he could make better gadgets.

Newton's mother had married a local vicar and gone to live with him when Newton was only four, leaving him in the care of his grandmother: this may well have had a traumatic effect on him, affecting his later relationships with people.

When he was in his early teens, however, his stepfather having died, Isaac had to return to Woolsthorpe to help with the farm. He was of less use than his mother had hoped. When tending sheep, for example, he would get so engrossed with a book, some invention, or in watching the stream, that the sheep would very likely get into the corn. Once, when returning from Grantham, he dismounted for a hill, forgot to remount and plodded home leading the horse, deep in thought. Throughout his life, Newton had the reputation of being a true absent-minded professor.

His schoolmaster recognized the intellect that was within Newton, and persuaded his mother to let him return to school. When Isaac eventually went to university at Cambridge, the farm workers reckoned that was all he was good for, and would never make anything of himself.

Newton's degree was undistinguished, but at Cambridge he met Isaac Barrow, then professor of mathematics, who must have sparked off something within Newton for shortly afterwards the dreamy-eyed boy began to concentrate on his most original work. In his graduation year, 1665, when Newton was 23, bubonic plague broke out in England and he returned to Woolsthorpe to avoid it. It was here that all the influences on him had their effect: he looked back on those two years of seclusion at his mother's cottage as the most significant of his life.

Isaac Newton himself was the source of the famous story that while sitting in the orchard on a warm autumn afternoon, the fall of an apple to the ground set him wondering about the nature of gravity. Talking later, he said that he wondered why the apple always fell towards the centre of the Earth, and reasoned that all matter attracts the rest of matter to it.

At Woolsthorpe, too, he performed his experiments on the nature of light, passing white light through a PRISM to produce a *spectrum* (Newton's word) of colours. He realized that white light is no more than all the colours seen together, and made many more investigations into the nature of LIGHT and OPTICS.

All this time, he was developing his ideas on MATHEMATICS, resulting in the discovery of the *calculus* or, as he called it, the 'Method of Fluxions'.

On Newton's return to Cambridge, Barrow stepped down in favour of him as professor of mathematics. One might imagine that Newton would publish the results of his work as soon as possible; actually he seems to have had little desire to publish, and when he did produce his results it was only at the insistence of others.

Newton's introduction into the full swing of academic life came with his election to the Royal Society in 1672 when he made the first working reflecting ASTRONOMICAL TELESCOPE. He gave a paper reporting his works on optics, and at once fell foul of Robert HOOKE, who upheld the wave theory of light as against Newton's corpuscular theory. Actually, both were right in their own way (see QUANTUM THEORY).

Newton's Opticks, not published until 1704, after his arch-enemy Hooke had died. Only then would Newton accept the presidency of the Royal Society, though he had been a leading member for over 30 years. In 1705 he became the first scientist to be knighted.

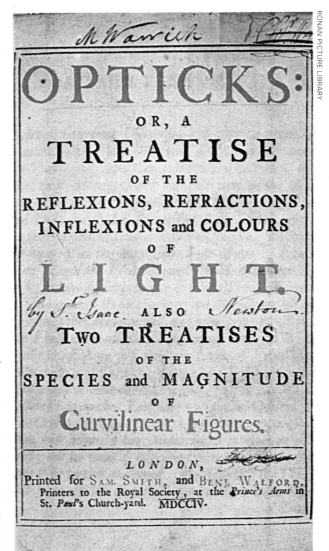

Hooke and Newton quarrelled many times over the years; there were also bitter debates as to whether Newton or the German mathematician Leibniz had invented the calculus. The truth is that many of Newton's discoveries were in the air at the time, and would before long have been put forward by others; but Newton's skill and genius tied the loose ends together to produce the final results.

The *Principia*, which describes the works on DYNAMICS summarized by NEWTON'S LAWS of Motion and Gravitation, was published in 1684, and *Opticks* in 1704. By this time Newton, seeking a more prominent situation than that of a mere academic, took on an important post at the Royal Mint, where he played a large part in revising the coinage system.

Newton never married, though there were romantic tales of a childhood sweetheart. He seems to have reserved his attentions for work only. He spent a vast amount of time studying theology, ALCHEMY, and the chronology of ancient civilizations, but his work on these subjects is now practically forgotten. In his own day, as now, his work on physics and mathematics made him an internationally renowned figure. When he died in 1727, he was buried in Westminster Abbey, an honour previously reserved for monarchs, politicians, soldiers, and other such worthies.

SCALA

Above right: Isaac Newton when he was 60, in 1702, a copy of Godfrey Kneller's portrait. Newton was grey before he was 40; here he wears a wig. About this time, he had changed from being a withdrawn academic to a hardened administrator, used to dealing with the coin clippers and counterfeiters who were prosecuted by the Mint.

Hooke's death ended one quarrel, but that with Leibniz was just beginning. The duel was won by Newton's immense prestige, and the strain killed Leibniz. One famous anecdote about Newton concerns a problem set by another great mathematician, Bernoulli, for the attention of Europe's greatest minds. Newton solved the problem in an evening after work at the Mint, before going to bed. When the result was published anonymously, Bernoulli is said to have remarked 'the lion is known by his claw': only Newton could have solved it so quickly.

Right: the reflecting telescope made by Newton for the Royal Society. The system is still known as the Newtonian design. This telescope has a concave mirror of 1.3 inches (3.4 cm) diameter and just over 6 inches (15 cm) focal length.

COOPER · BRIDGEMAN LIBRARY / THE ROYAL SOCIETY

NEWTON'S LAWS

In the course of his pioneering experiments in many branches of science, Sir Isaac Newton discovered several of the fundamental laws of PHYSICS. A scientific 'law' is a general statement which can explain the results of a number of different experiments; this generalization can then be used to *predict* the outcome of other, similar, experiments.

The basic principles of DYNAMICS (the study of how forces act on objects) are summed up in Newton's three Laws of Motion.

Laws of Motion Newton's First Law says that *any moving body will continue to move in a straight line and at a constant speed unless it is acted upon by an outside force.* This is not immediately obvious, since on Earth we are used to moving objects eventually stopping. But this is because outside forces, such as friction and air resistance, act on the body to slow it down.

What happens when, as in most practical cases, an outside force does act on a moving body is covered by the Second Law: *if a force is applied to a body, its momentum will change in such a way that the rate of change of momentum is equal to the magnitude of the force.* The momentum is the mass of the body multiplied by its velocity (speed), and so another way of stating the second Law

is that *the force on a body is equal to the mass of the body multiplied by the acceleration produced by the force:* Force = mass × acceleration. A consequence of this law is that if the same force is applied to two objects with different masses, the less massive body will accelerate more than the more massive one.

The Third Law states that *for every action there is an equal and opposite reaction.* The action and reaction refer to the forces on two different bodies; for example, the weight of a chair standing on a floor must be balanced by an upward 'reaction' force of the floor on the chair, or else (according to the second Law) the chair would be accelerated towards the centre of the Earth.

Anyone who tries to jump off a stationary toboggan notices an effect of the Third Law: the toboggan begins to move in the opposite direction even before the person's feet touch the ground.

The action of a rocket demonstrates all the laws of motion.

Newton's work on gravitation was inspired, he maintained, by seeing the fall of an apple. From this he reasoned that the force which attracted the apple towards the Earth's centre was the same one which held the Moon in its orbit around Earth. This 'giant leap' in thought culminated in the Apollo Moon missions, 300 years later.

PHOTRI

A rocket at rest on the ground, or coasting through space with the engine switched off, is obeying the First Law. When the engine is on, the force with which the propellant is ejected from the rocket must be balanced by a reaction force of the propellant on the rocket, and it is this reaction force which drives the rocket forward. These two forces must be equal, and act in opposite directions (Third Law). Since the mass of the rocket is much greater than that of the ejected propellant, the rocket is accelerated to a very much slower velocity than that of the propellant (Second Law).

Gravitation Newton's Law of Gravitation describes how the gravitational force between any two objects varies with their masses and the distance between them. Each body experiences a force equal to the product of the masses of the two bodies multiplied by the universal Constant of Gravitation,

G, and divided by the square of their separation. Newton was unable to explain the origin of gravitation, and Einstein's General Theory of RELATIVITY (1915) proposed that the geometry of space near massive bodies is altered, so that the quickest distance (the *geodesic*) between two points is not a straight line. By substituting the word 'geodesic' for 'straight line' in Newton's First Law, Einstein was able to incorporate gravity in the First Law of Motion. In spite of relativity,

Below: the inverse square law of gravitation elongates the waters of the Earth, but the Earth cannot distort in the same way; the result is two 'heaps' of water—the tides. Lower picture: the way a body cools, when in an air flow, is shown by an exponential curve. Below right: Newton's laws of motion can be applied wherever moving bodies are concerned – such as in this game of bowls.

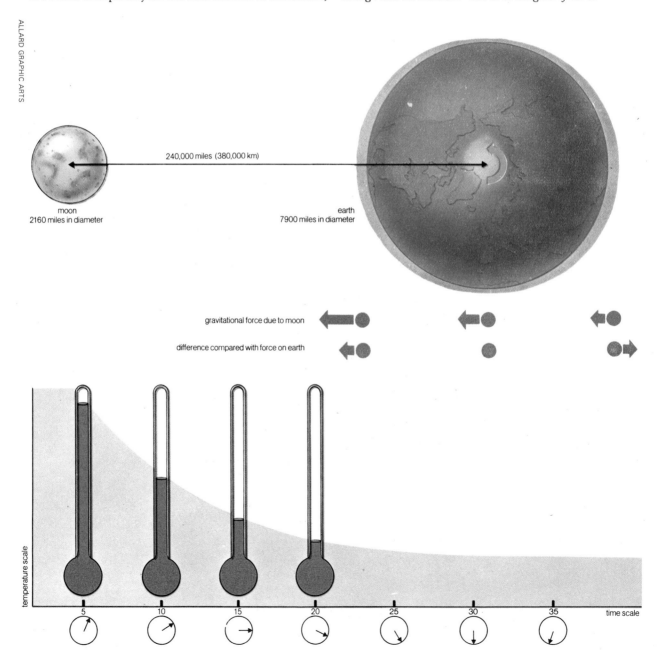

ALLARD GRAPHIC ARTS

240,000 miles (380,000 km)

moon
2160 miles in diameter

earth
7900 miles in diameter

gravitational force due to moon

difference compared with force on earth

temperature scale

5   10   15   20   25   30   35   time scale

however, the Second and Third Laws are still, three hundred years after their formulation, fundamental to modern science.

Cooling Newton's investigations of the cooling of a hot body led to his law of cooling: *the rate of cooling is proportional to the difference in temperature between the object and its surroundings.* The rate of cooling is measured by the rate at which the temperature of a body falls; so a body at a high temperature relative to its surroundings will initially cool fast, and its temperature falls rapidly. As its temperature decreases, however, the cooling becomes slower, and so the temperature falls less rapidly. This type of behaviour is known as an *exponential decay* (explained in LOGARITHM) and strictly speaking, although the temperature of the body becomes closer and closer to that of the surroundings, it will never become exactly the same.

NICKEL

Early copper miners in the Harz Mountains in Germany came across some ore which they were unable to smelt successfully, obtaining only a light yellow, brittle and useless product. They put the blame on the devil and called the ore 'Kupfernickel' (Old Nick's copper). When, in 1751, Cronstedt first isolated the additional element in the ore which had caused the trouble he called it nickel. It was not until 150 years later that nickel was first extracted on a commercial scale.

The metal itself is silvery white and is noted for its corrosion resistance and its ability to retain good mechanical strength up

Below: pellets of nickel produced by the Mond carbonyl process. Nickel carbonyl is decomposed on to circulating 'seed' pellets which are removed when they have grown to the correct size.

to temperatures of the order of 1000°C (1800°F). Like iron and cobalt it is *ferromagnetic* (see MAGNETISM). Over one half of all nickel produced is used for alloying with iron to make steels having superior resistance to high temperature oxidation and chemical attack or simply having better mechanical properties.

Occurrence and extraction

The vast majority of the world's nickel is mined in Canada. There is a huge deposit of mixed nickel and copper sulphide at Sudbury, Ontario and a deposit of similar ore in Manitoba. Outside Canada there are deposits of a nickel-containing silica ore, containing considerable amounts of iron but no copper, at New Caledonia in the South Pacific, and in Cuba.

The first stages of the extraction of nickel from sulphide ores are similar to those used for smelting COPPER. The ore is first crushed and the sulphides concentrated using the flotation process. The mixed nickel copper and iron sulphides are then smelted to form a sulphide *matte*. It is not possible to produce nickel simply by roasting the matte in air because much of the nickel would be oxidized before all the sulphur was removed as sulphur dioxide. The matte is partially roasted, however, to oxidize the iron sulphide to iron oxide which is removed in a silicate slag. The molten matte of mixed nickel and copper sulphides is poured into a mould and slowly cooled to form crystals of the two sulphides, which are then crushed, ground,

and separated using a flotation process and the nickel sulphide, NiS, is sintered to form nickel oxide, NiO.

The nickel oxide sinter is next treated with sulphuric acid to remove the remaining copper sulphate and then reduced to nickel at 350°C (662°F) by a stream of *producer gas* (a mixture of hydrogen and carbon monoxide). The nickel is refined either electrolytically (see ELECTROLYSIS), or by the Mond carbonyl process in which nickel powder is exposed to producer gas, but this time at 50°C (122°F). The result is the production of volatile nickel carbonyl, $Ni(CO)_4$, which is passed into a decomposition tower where it dissociates at 180°C (356°F) and pure nickel is deposited as pellets.

A *hydrometallurgical* method for the extraction of nickel from mixed sulphides is rapidly replacing the more traditional processes. It is based on the ability of the mixed sulphides to dissolve in an ammoniacal solution (a solution containing ammonium IONS, NH_4^+) in the presence of air at 125 psi (8.62 bar). The iron sulphide is converted to ferric hydroxide, which is filtered off together with other insoluble solids and the solution boiled to reprecipitate the copper as copper sulphide which is similarly removed. The nickel itself is precipitated as the metal by treating the solution with hydrogen at 150°C (302°F) and 750 psi (51.7 bar). The process is also capable of extracting cobalt if it is present in the ore.

Above left: a support in the superheater of a large marine boiler. The support is cast from an alloy containing nickel and chromium in equal proportions, and it remains serviceable after four years use. One of the most important uses of nickel is in making alloys which can withstand very high temperatures without being oxidized.

Left: a modern nickel smelting furnace. The picture shows a top blown rotary converter—the first of its kind to be used commercially for smelting metals other than iron. The furnace weighs 226 tons and can accept a charge of ore weighing 50 tons. The heating zone (right) is shaped like the bowl of a concrete mixer and can be rotated at speeds of up to 40 rpm. Oxygen is blown into the molten nickel sulphide ore to convert it into metallic nickel.

Right: one of the storage tanks in a ship for transporting liquefied natural gas. The tank is formed of nickel-containing stainless steel plates which are sufficiently flexible to allow for expansion and contraction of the tank as it heats up and cools down.

Uses of nickel A significant proportion of the world's output of nickel is ELECTROPLATED on to base metals to provide corrosion resistance; it is also sometimes covered with a very thin 'flash' layer of CHROMIUM to give a brilliant and tarnish resistant finish. Vessels which have to resist corrosion over long periods may be made from pure nickel or nickel clad steel; this is especially the case in the food industry where the non-toxicity of the metal is a particular asset. The pure metal is also used in a powdered form as a CATALYST where its ability to 'activate' hydrogen is exploited in processes which convert unsaturated hydrocarbons into solid fats such as MARGARINE.

Primarily however, nickel is used as an alloying element. Historically the first nickel ALLOYS were the direct results of smelting impure or mixed ores. For example, some coins produced in 235 BC were made from a copper-nickel alloy containing 20% nickel; a composition remarkably similar to that used for modern cupro-nickel coinage (25% nickel). Another copper-nickel alloy was produced in 1905 by directly smelting a mixed ore. It was called 'Monel Metal', contained 68% nickel, and combined the excellent corrosion resistance of the pure metal with better mechanical properties. Cupro-nickels with 20 to 30% nickel and sometimes up to 10% iron possess a useful combination of strength, ductility and corrosion resistance. They are widely used in marine environments and for condenser tubes in distillation apparatus.

Nickel silver is an attractive white alloy of copper containing 18% nickel and 18% zinc. For domestic use it is often electroplated with a thin layer of pure silver to make the familiar EPNS (electroplated nickel silver) ware.

The majority of nickel produced is used for improving the properties of steels and cast irons. Nickel steels contain between 0.5% and 10% nickel and show superior strength and ductility. This is because nickel increases the 'hardenability' of steel, enabling thicker sections to be effectively HEAT TREATED and also reducing the necessity for rapid quenching which can lead to cracking. In cast irons nickel encourages the precipitation of graphite as well as increasing the hardness of the matrix. Nickel is also used as a component of stainless steels containing 10 to 12% chromium. Its presence in amounts exceeding 8% changes the CRYSTAL structure of the steel from *body centred cubic* to *face centred cubic*, and as a result renders it much more ductile and easily workable. The most common stainless steel contains 18% chromium and 8% nickel.

Nickel is widely used as a base metal in alloys which have to resist oxidation and still maintain strength when red hot. The binary alloy Nichrome contains 20% chromium in nickel and is used for electric fire heating elements, among other things. Attempts to improve the mechanical strength of Nichrome by precipitation hardening has led to the development of the Nimonic (a trade mark) alloys, used for components such as turbine blades of jet engines, where the best possible combination of high temperature strength and oxidation resistance is required. The Nimonic or 'Superalloys' have additions of titanium and aluminium which form the strength giving precipitates.

An alloy of 36% nickel in iron is unique in that it has a zero coefficient of thermal expansion, in other words it does not expand when heated. Under the trade name of 'Invar' it is used for standards of length, measuring tapes, pendulums and precision machine components. The addition of 12% chromium forms another alloy, 'Elinvar', whose elasticity is independant of temperature. It is used for watch hair springs, and in weighing machines and other measuring devices.

Above: a contemporary mezzotint portrait of Niépce, made around 1800, when he was in his thirties.

Below: the earliest surviving picture taken by Niépce, dating from 1827 and showing the view over the rooftops from his window. The strange lighting is partly caused by the eight-hour exposure, during which the sun moved round, and partly by the photographic materials: white bitumen of Judea on dark grey pewter.

NIEPCE, Joseph Nicéphore (1765–1833)

Seven years after the nineteenth century began, Joseph Niépce and his elder brother Claude patented a marine INTERNAL COMBUSTION ENGINE, pre-dating that of DIESEL by about 90 years. It worked so well that the brothers confidently expected its instant purchase by manufacturers, but Claude spent most of the rest of his life unsuccessfully trying to exploit it in his native France and abroad. The credit for the other great Niépce discovery therefore belongs solely to Joseph, although Claude undoubtedly made some contribution. They christened the invention 'heliography'. We call it photography.

When Claude and Joseph served in the post-Revolutionary armed forces, the latter took an additional name, Nicéphore ('bringer of victory'), by which he is usually known. He caught typhoid in the south of France and, as the military hospital was full, he was nursed by a local family. He married their daughter and, when he was invalided out of the army, brought her to his home town, Châlon-sur-Sâone, Burgundy. Later, Etiene MAREY and Louis and Auguste LUMIERE also lived in Burgundy, so it is an important place in photographic history.

Niépce interested himself in lithography and his attempts, begun in 1816, to copy engravings on to light-sensitive plates, were his first photographic experiments. They were similar to those of two Englishmen: Thomas Wedgwood, in the 1790s, and William Henry Fox Talbot, inventor of the negative-positive process on which modern photography is based.

At first, Niépce sensitized his plates with silver salts, which had been known for two hundred years to darken when exposed to sunlight. But his experiments failed in the same way as those of Wedgwood: without the right chemical to stop the darkening at the precise moment that the required image appeared, the process went on until the plate was black all over. Within three years, Sir John HERSCHEL observed that sodium thiosulphate (it was called 'hyposulphite' at the time, thus 'hypo'), stopped the darkening, so 'fixing' the image. But it was too late for Niépce, who had already turned to bitumen of Judea, an asphalt-like substance which he must have known well from its common use in lithography, and which hardens and does not change colour. With it, he made successful copies of engravings in 1822. The process was a direct positive one, since the hardened bitumen, representing the highlights, was white against a darkened metal background.

Niépce conceived the same idea as Talbot had a decade later: if he could copy and fix engravings, why not do the same with life itself? He set to work to capture the images of the CAMERA OBSCURA by heliography. Over the next few years, he took a gradually improving series of views from his study window, finally getting a result he could call successful in 1826. It needed an exposure of about eight hours. These views, of which one still exists, were the world's first permanent photographs 'from nature' though, being made of bitumen of Judea on pewter, they in no way led to modern photographic technology.

But heliography did lead to the workable process developed by Louis DAGUERRE, who had become Niépce's partner in 1829. Six years before daguerreotypes were revealed to the public, Niépce died. Had he lived until that exciting year of 1839, those beautiful and sharp pictures—which were to dominate photography for the next twenty years—might have been known by his name rather than by Daguerre's.

NIGHT VISION EQUIPMENT (see image intensifier)

NITROGEN

Nitrogen, N_2, is a colourless, odourless gas that forms more than 75% of the Earth's atmosphere. It was first discovered in 1772 by the Swedish chemist C W Scheele who recognized that air was composed of two different gases, one that would support combustion and respiration (OXYGEN) and one that would not (nitrogen). He was able to obtain nitrogen by burning a substance in a closed chamber filled with air; the combustion removed the oxygen leaving nitrogen behind. The principal naturally occurring nitrogen compounds are *saltpetre* (potassium nitrate KNO_3) which is found in Spain, Italy and Egypt, and *Chile saltpetre* (sodium nitrate, $NaNO_3$). Nitrogen has two stable ISOTOPES, N-14 and N-15, the former being more than 250 times more abundant than the latter. It is an important constituent of living tissue (PROTEINS are composed of nitrogen-containing AMINO ACID units) and for this reason many agricultural FERTILIZERS, for example ammonium nitrate, NH_4NO_3, contain a high proportion of nitrogen.

Production Since nitrogen has a lower boiling point ($-196°C$, $-321°F$) than oxygen ($-183°C$, $-297°F$), liquid air can be separated into its components by *fractional* DISTILLATION, and this is the method used to make nitrogen on an industrial scale. Nitrogen gas is marketed in steel cylinders under a pressure of about 120 atmospheres, and it often contains small amounts of neon and helium (see INERT GASES) which are present in very small quantities in the air. Many instruments used in research and industry, for example *mass*

Below: an illustration by George Cruikshank for a book published in 1834 showing the effects of nitrous oxide, or 'laughing gas'. The gas is widely used today as an anaesthetic.

spectrometers (see MASS SPECTROSCOPY), rely on a high vacuum for their operation. To ensure that the vacuum is as perfect as possible, part of the vacuum chamber is cooled with liquid nitrogen to 'freeze out' remaining traces of carbon dioxide, water vapour and other volatile substances which may be present. Liquid nitrogen for this and other purposes is supplied in metal vacuum flasks, called *Dewar flasks*. Small quantities of very pure nitrogen can be obtained by chemical methods, for example by heating *sodium azide* in a vacuum:

$$2NaN_3 \rightarrow 2Na + 3N_2$$
sodium azide   sodium   nitrogen

Nitrogen gas is chemically relatively inert, and for this reason it has been used in certain metallurgical processes and in incandescent tungsten filament lamps to prevent OXIDATION.

Nowadays, however, argon, which is even less reactive than nitrogen, is used more often where an inert atmosphere is required.

Nitrogen compounds For many years the most important nitrogen-containing compounds were potassium nitrate, a component of gunpowder (see EXPLOSIVES), and sodium nitrate, which both occur naturally. Nitric ACID, HNO_3, was first prepared in 1648 by treating sodium nitrate with concentrated sulphuric acid, and this process remained in use for many years until AMMONIA, NH_3, became a readily available raw material. The modern method of making nitric acid is by oxidizing ammonia in the presence of a PLATINUM-rhodium CATALYST. Most nitrogen-containing compounds derive their nitrogen either directly or indirectly from am-

Below: a road tanker being filled with liquid nitrogen. Because of the extremely low temperature of liquid nitrogen, water vapour and carbon dioxide freeze out on to the delivery pipe.

Below centre: meat is preserved by freezing with liquid nitrogen. The very low temperature of liquid nitrogen ensures that the meat is frozen quickly, thus minimizing damage to the meat cells.

monia, which is made by the Haber-Bosch process. Nitrogen gas reacts directly with HYDROGEN in the presence of an iron oxide catalyst according to the following equation:

$$N_2 \quad + \quad 3H_2 \quad \rightarrow \quad 2NH_3$$

nitrogen   hydrogen   ammonia

Because nitrogen is relatively inert the reaction must be conducted at a high temperature—about 500°C (900°F)—and pressure—from 200 to 1000 times atmospheric pressure.

Ammonia is a gas at room temperature, but it dissolves very easily in water to give a mildly alkaline solution containing *ammonium* IONS, NH_4^+, and *hydroxide* ions, OH^-. Such solutions can be neutralized with acids to give ammonium SALTS which are ionic crystalline solids. Neutralization with hydrochloric acid, for example, gives the salt ammonium

Below right: a windscreen for the European Airbus positioned in a test chamber. Liquid nitrogen is pumped into the chamber to simulate the low temperatures experienced at high altitudes.

chloride, NH_4Cl, which is sometimes called *sal ammoniac*:

$$NH_4OH \quad + \quad HCl \quad \rightarrow \quad NH_4Cl \quad + \quad H_2O$$

ammonium   hydrochloric   ammonium   water
hydroxide   acid   chloride

Ammonium chloride is used as a *flux* in SOLDERING and GALVANIZING processes since it reacts at high temperatures with metal corrosion products, thereby cleaning the surfaces being soldered or galvanized. It is also used as the electrolyte in BATTERIES of the Leclanché type, in the manufacture of dyes, and in various cough and cold remedies. Another ammonium salt, ammonium nitrate, NH_4NO_3, is important as a fertilizer and as a component of various explosive compositions.

Hydrazine, N_2H_4, and *hydrazoic* acid, HN_3, are highly reactive compounds containing only nitrogen and hydrogen. Hydrazine is used in conjunction with *nitrogen tetroxide*, N_2O_4, as a rocket propellant, and a fuel of this type was used both in the service module and the lunar excursion module (LEM) of the Apollo moon programme. The chief use of hydrazoic acid is in the

preparation of *lead azide*, $Pb(N_3)_2$, which is a pressure sensitive compound used in explosive DETONATORS:

$$Pb + 2HN_3 \rightarrow Pb(N_3)_2 + H_2$$
lead   hydrazoic   lead azide   hydrogen
acid

Probably the best known oxide of nitrogen is *nitrous oxide*, N_2O, which is a widely used ANAESTHETIC gas. It is called 'laughing gas' because of the unusual side effects which sometimes precede anaesthesia, and it can be prepared by heating ammonium nitrate:

$$NH_4NO_3 \rightarrow N_2O + 2H_2O$$
ammonium   nitrous   water
nitrate   oxide

Before it can be used as an anaesthetic, the gas must be carefully purified to remove traces of other oxides such as nitric oxide, NO, and nitrogen dioxide, NO_2, which are toxic.

Boron nitride, BN, is a crystalline compound which normally resembles graphite (see CARBON). It can, however, be converted at very high temperature ($1800°C$, $3272°F$) and pressure ($85,000$ times atmospheric pressure) to a second crystalline form called *borazon*. Borazon has the same crystal structure as DIAMOND and is very nearly as hard.

Organic compounds

Nitrogen-containing organic compounds are very common and are classified according to the particular nitrogen-containing groups they contain. Thus, AMINES contain $-NH_2$ groups, *amides* contain $-CONH_2$ groups, *cyanates* contain $-CNO$ groups, *cyanides* contain $-CN$ groups, *isocyanates* contain $-NCO$ groups, *isocyanides* contain $-NC$ groups and *nitro* compounds contain $-NO_2$ groups.

Many explosives such as *trinitrotoluene* (TNT), $C_6H_2(CH_3)-(NO_2)_3$, and *picric acid*, $C_6H_2(OH)(NO_2)_3$, are organic nitro compounds. TNT is prepared by treating the HYDROCARBON toluene with a mixture of concentrated nitric and sulphuric acids. During the reaction nitro groups are introduced one by one into the toluene molecule, and the compounds *mononitrotoluene*, $C_6H_4(CH_3)(NO_2)$, and *dinitrotoluene*, $C_6H_3(CH_3)(NO_2)_2$, can be isolated as intermediates. Aniline, $C_6H_5NH_2$, an important amine which is used in the manufacture of dyestuffs is prepared by reducing *nitrobenzene*, $C_6H_5NO_2$, using iron shavings and weak acid. Isocyanates are used in the manufacture of *polyurethane* PLASTICS.

Below: steel shafts are cooled in liquid nitrogen and then fitted into the gearwheel apertures. The gearwheels become tightly secured to the shafts as the latter expand on warming to room temperature.

BRITISH OXYGEN CO

NOBEL, Alfred Bernhard (1833–1896)

Alfred Nobel's name is perpetuated in the Nobel prizes for science, literature and peace, yet during the course of his life as a prolific inventor perhaps his most notable achievement was the development of dynamite, first patented in Britain in 1867 and in the USA in 1868.

He was born in Stockholm on 21 October 1833, the third son of Immanuel Nobel, a highly talented inventor and engineer who, although he went bankrupt in both his native Sweden and in Russia, contributed a great deal to both countries, especially in armaments. Alfred travelled widely, spending a year in the USA, and in spite of his lack of formal education became fluent in five languages.

His first patent, for a kind of gasholder, was granted in 1857, but he devoted most of his energies to the study of EXPLOSIVES, particularly nitroglycerine. Despite a disastrous explosion in 1864 which killed his younger brother and four other people, he developed a DETONATOR using fulminate of mercury which made possible the commercial exploitation of explosives which did not explode with simple ignition.

He was determined to discover a method whereby the extremely potent but dangerous liquid nitroglycerine could be handled with reasonable safety. In 1866 he found that, by the addition of kieselguhr (diatomaceous earth), which acted as an absorbent, it was possible to produce a solid blasting substance which could be manufactured and used with relative safety, with the reduction in the explosive force of only 25%.

Following the immediate success of dynamite, Nobel continued his work on explosives and in 1875 introduced blasting gelatine, made by combining nitroglycerine with guncotton to produce an even more powerful explosive.

In 1871 he came to Britain and formed the Nobel's Explosives Co Ltd, which opened a factory at Ardeer in the west of Scotland. He had a laboratory in Hamburg from 1865 to 1872, and he worked in Paris from 1873 to 1890, but the last years of his life were spent mostly in San Remo, Italy.

In 1887 he discovered *ballistite*, a military explosive that was one of the first smokeless powders and which greatly reduced the smoke cloud that had until then accompanied the firing of any piece of artillery. First used by the Italians, ballistite was a predecessor of cordite, and Nobel fought bitterly with the British government to prove that cordite infringed his ballistite patents, but he finally lost the case in 1895. Cordite is still used as a propellant.

The total number of patents granted to Nobel, throughout the world, was an impressive 355. He amassed a fortune through his inventions, and added to it with his investments in the Bofors munitions works in Sweden and in the Romanian oil fields at Baku which were run by his elder brothers Ludvig and Robert.

He was a lonely man who never married and who suffered from chronic illness most of his life. His cynicism and pessimism concealed his idealistic and benevolent nature, but perhaps also explain the apparent contradiction between his contributions to the armaments industry and the provision in his will for the vast bulk of his estate to be used for the establishment of the five world-renowned prizes named after him. These prizes, for physics, chemistry, physiology or medicine, literature and peace, were first awarded in 1901. The Nobel Foundation and the Bank of Sweden added a sixth prize, for economics, in 1969. Each award consists of a gold medal, a diploma and money. Alfred Nobel died in San Remo on 10 December 1896.

Left: an 1897 photograph of Nobel's factory at Ardeer, Scotland. Dynamite is being mixed by hand. The floor is covered in sand, in order to allow any spilt explosive to be easily swept up. This primitive precaution would not be considered satisfactory in a modern explosive factory.

Below: a portrait of Nobel by Professor Östermann.

NOISE MEASUREMENT

One definition of *noise* is that it is all unwanted sounds. The analysis and measurement of noise originally developed with the growth of electrical and electronic communications systems, such as the telephone and radio, where electrical noise could seriously distort a transmitted signal and, if very large, could completely 'mask' or swamp it. Parallel to this has grown an interest in sound noise in the human environment. Apart from its effects on communications, noise can produce undesirable psychological effects in people and very loud noise can produce physical damage to the ears.

Noise energy and frequency What distinguishes a noise from a signal (such as speech) is that the signal contains wanted information—that is, it has a structure—whereas noise contains no information; it sometimes has no regular structure and is then said to be *random*. Two important features of noise, however, can be determined: the *total energy* and the *frequency content*.

Total energy gives an overall figure of the 'strength' of a noise and is important when considering, for example, its physical effects. *Frequency analysis* becomes important when considering different types of sounds. A truck struggling uphill produces low frequency sounds but a jet has a shrill high frequency whine.

The human ear, however, is not so sensitive to low frequency sounds and the total energy of a particular noise may not directly relate to its physical or psychological effects. To obtain a figure which represents the 'effect' of a sound on an average person entails adjusting (*weighting*) the magnitude of the frequency components of the noise by a factor that corresponds to the sensitivity of the ear at each frequency. A figure of the receptiveness of the ear to the whole noise can be obtained by summation of all these adjusted magnitudes.

Measurement of sound energy Noise energy E_N is measured on a LOGARITHMIC scale relative to a reference sound energy E_R. This reference point is usually taken to be the quietest sound which can normally be heard. The noise is then measured in *decibels* (or dB for short) and is determined from the expression $10 \times \log E_N/E_R$. But energy levels are difficult to measure directly, whereas the PRESSURE of a sound wave is more easily determined. Sound energy is related to the *square* of the pressure so that an alternative expression for dB rating of a noise is $10 \times \log (P_N/P_R)^2$, which is equal to $20 \times \log P_N/P_R$.

The quietest sound that can normally be heard (the threshold of hearing) is at a pressure of 0.00002 N/m^2 (20 thousand millionths of an atmosphere) and this is the reference pressure P_R. A sound wave with a pressure equal to P_R is therefore rated as zero dB (the logarithm of one is always zero).

For comparison, the normal atmospheric pressure is one atmosphere, which is 100,000 N/m^2 or 194 dB. The pressure ratio of one million to one over the audible region is one reason for using the decibel scale, since the wide pressure range is compressed into a more convenient numerical range of 0 to 120 dB. It is also convenient that, over much of the range, one decibel is about the minimum noise level difference that can be detected, while a doubling of loudness corresponds to a change of 10 dB.

Measuring apparatus The basic instrumentation for noise measurement consists of a sound level meter. The diaphragm of the MICROPHONE responds to pressure fluctuations in the air (that is, sound waves) and the resulting movement of the diaphragm is converted into an electrical signal, which can be amplified and processed as required. The signal from the microphone passes first to an AMPLIFIER stage and then to an attenuator (reducer) which is calibrated in decibels. The output from the attenuator may be fed as desired to one of the four types of weighting networks, which are electrical FILTER networks. These are referred to as A, B, C and D. The particular frequency response of the network chosen modifies the input signal accordingly.

'Weighting A' is the most widely used and sound levels measured in this way are referred to as 'decibels A' or 'dBA'. The advantage of the A weighting is that dBA levels have been found to correspond fairly closely with subjective effects, since people are less sensitive to low frequency sounds. The B network is of very little contemporary use. The C network is used when it is required to have a wideband measurement of the noise. The D network was designed for use with aircraft noise—the rise at a few thousand hertz emphasizing the disturbing compressor noise whine of jet engines. The dBD reading is related to the *perceived noise level*, or PNdB, which is used for aircraft noise measurement.

The electrical signal from the weighting network is passed to a RECTIFIER and smoothing network, which averages out the rapid waveform fluctuations. It is then fed to a *moving coil* indicating meter which is part of the sound level meter. The meter scale is calibrated in decibels.

Typical noise levels The threshold of hearing is defined as zero decibel level (0.00002 N/m²), a whisper at 30 dBA (0.00063 N/m²), normal conversation at about 60 dBA (0.02 N/m²) and a busy street at about 80 dBA (0.2 N/m²). A motor horn has a noise level about 100 dBA (2 N/m²) close to the vehicle and a thunder clap about 120 dBA (20 N/m²). A

sustained level of 120 dBA would produce a sensation of feeling in the ear and further increase will cause pain. A level of 90 dBA sustained for 8 hours a day 5 days a week is currently accepted as the limit which should not be exceeded in order to avoid excessive noise induced hearing loss, while the unprotected ear should not be exposed to peak levels greater than 135 dBA.

NON-DESTRUCTIVE TESTING (see quality control)

Noise measurements are made in various industrial and commercial locations because noise intensities greater than 120 dBA will cause pain and damage to the ears. The sound level meter may be tripod-mounted (see above and below right) or hand-held (below left). The black sphere on the end of the microphone (below right) is a wind shield. Aircraft noises are high in frequency.

CAMERA PRESS/B S S R S

NON-LETHAL WEAPONS

More and more riot control weapons are becoming available, and the occasions which civil authorities believe justify their use are increasingly frequent. The theory of 'technological' riot control is to use weapons which, while making life so unpleasant for the rioters as to halt the disturbance, do no permanent damage. In fact the line between these two demands is so slim that many scientists believe it to be non-existent.

Anti-riot gases CS gas is perhaps the best known, and most widely used, new riot weapon. It was devised by the Chemical Defence Experimental Establishment at Porton Down, England to replace ordinary tear gas (CN gas). CS (chloracetophenone) is a stable off-white powder dispersed by a pyrotechnic charge in a grenade or canister. The British army in Ulster had fired 12,500 CS grenades or cartridges by 1970. CS gas cartridges may be fired from standard 1.5 inch (38 mm) pistols and anti-riot guns with a range of 120 yards (100 m). After a delay of about two seconds, the cartridge releases gas for 5 to 25 seconds.

According to the patents taken out by the Porton Down researchers: 'In addition to causing pain in the eyes, tears and spasms of the eyelids, CS also produces a sharp burning pain in the nose, throat and chest which becomes worse and causes a

Below: anti-riot gun of a type used by the army against civilians. It is constructed mainly of high tensile aluminium alloy and fires cartridges of CS gas or rubber bullets.

Left: an armoured vehicle aims a water cannon, basically a high-pressure hose which emits a jet of water, at a defiant youth.

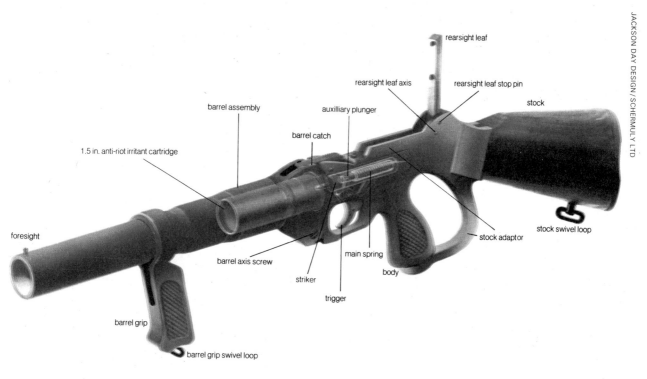

JACKSON DAY DESIGN/SCHERMULY LTD

rearsight leaf

rearsight leaf axis

rearsight leaf stop pin

stock

barrel assembly

auxilliary plunger

barrel catch

1.5 in. anti-riot irritant cartridge

foresight

stock swivel loop

barrel axis screw

stock adaptor

main spring

striker

body

trigger

barrel grip

barrel grip swivel loop

choking sensation. Although breathing is not actually interfered with, it is rendered extremely painful'. The patent says that CS gas has no permanent effects. But the research on which this conclusion is based is still secret. There have been reports from Ulster of CS gas causing unconsciousness, acute bronchial disorders, and lung damage particularly in the very young, old, and infirm. In high concentrations it is fatal.

There is now a new riot gas, CR gas, which will eventually replace CS. It can be dissolved in liquid (and therefore used in a water cannon) or in a jelly to produce 'riot barriers'. CR (dibenzoxazepine) irritates the eyes, skin and mucous membranes of the nose and throat. Eminent scientists are concerned that the long-term effects of this highly active chemical are not well enough known.

Other devices Another weapon familiar from Ulster is the rubber bullet, designed to break up riot crowds. This began life in Hong Kong in 1958 when police fired baton rounds—wooden cylinders—into rioting crowds. The rubber bullet was first used in 1970 in Ulster, being fired from a US Federal riot gun or signal pistol. The 5 oz (142 g) bullet travels with a velocity of 160 mph (257 km/h) and is so unstable in flight that the firer cannot hit a 2 yard (1.8 m) wide target only 20 yards (18 m) away. The army regulations governing rubber bullets say that they should not be fired at people closer than 25 yards (23 m) and should be fired into the ground so they lose some momentum. In Ulster both these rules have been broken—a third of the patients treated at a Belfast hospital for the effects of rubber bullets were shot from closer than 5 yards (4.6 m).

There are also less well-known anti-riot weapons such as the 'curdler', which consists of portable loudspeakers producing a shrieking noise of 90 decibels and 350 watts. The authoritative US National Science Foundation says that this weapon gives 'a severe risk of permanent impairment of hearing.' Another device, the 'stun gun', fires a 4 inch diameter spinning bag holding 8 oz (227 g) of shot. It is fatal when fired at people closer than 20 ft (6 m). Even more advanced is the 'tasser' which fires barbed electric contacts with a trailing wire. The barbs snag in clothing, and a current passes through the wire, paralyzing the victim.

The device which has attracted most attention is perhaps the *photic driver*. This is a combination of two attacks—a red light flashing on and off with a frequency between 10 and 30 Hz (cycles per second), and a loudspeaker emitting noise at 4 Hz. The effect of these stimuli is to induce nausea and panic. It may also cause epileptic fits in up to 1 in 20 of its victims—even if they have had no previous history of epilepsy.

Rubber bullets and the gun which fires them. The bullet itself is a hard-rubber blunt nosed cylinder which is fitted into a cartridge containing a small firing charge.

NUCLEAR MAGNETIC RESONANCE

Nuclear Magnetic Resonance, normally referred to as NMR, is a technique for measuring the magnetic properties of individual atomic nuclei. Since its discovery in 1945 NMR has become widely used in chemical ANALYSIS to determine the detailed structures of MOLECULES.

It is probably the most powerful single tool available to the chemist for determining the structure of a new compound, and is used wherever new compounds are synthesized, especially in the pharmaceutical industry and in university research laboratories. NMR has provided a great deal of information about the structures of the synthetic *polymers* which are the basis of PLASTICS. Another important application is in the analysis of natural products isolated from plants and animals. NMR is also used to investigate the metabolites or breakdown products of drugs in the body, although the very small quantities in which these can be obtained present great difficulties. Increasingly NMR is being applied to biological problems, for example studying the structure of PROTEINS and investigating the mode of action of enzymes.

The basis of NMR

The basis of the method is the interaction between certain kinds of atomic nuclei and magnetic fields (see MAGNETISM). Some nuclei behave as if they are spinning about an axis, and because they carry an electric charge they have a *magnetic moment*. These nuclei align themselves with a magnetic field in a similar way to the alignment of a compass needle in the Earth's magnetic field. In accordance with the QUANTUM THEORY, nuclei can take up only particular preferred orientations in a magnetic field. The most important cases are those nuclei which behave like magnetic *dipoles* and have just two orientations in a magnetic field. Among these are the common ISOTOPES of hydrogen, H-1, of fluorine, F-19,

and of phosphorus, P-31; and the rare isotope of carbon, C-13, which has a natural abundance of 1%.

Each orientation of the nuclei corresponds to a different *energy state*, the energy difference between the states being proportional to the strength of the magnetic field. If the nuclei are subjected to ELECTROMAGNETIC RADIATION with a frequency exactly equivalent to the separation between the energy states, the nuclei will be induced to change from one state to the other. The overall effect is that energy is absorbed by the nuclei at a frequency called the *resonance frequency*. The magnetic field strengths usually employed are such that absorption occurs at *radio frequencies*.

Absorption frequencies

The importance of NMR in chemical analysis is that for any isotope there is a range of absorption frequencies, depending on the chemical environments of the nuclei. The nuclei experience a magnetic field which differs slightly from the applied field because of shielding by the surrounding ELECTRONS. Different resonance frequencies are found for different compounds and also for nuclei in various locations within the same molecule. For example the hydrogen resonance of ethyl alcohol, CH_3CH_2OH, shows three separate absorption frequencies corresponding to the three types of hydrogen present. The separate absorptions have intensities proportional to the number of nuclei contributing, that is in the ratio 3:2:1.

A further important feature is that the signals have small splittings caused by interactions between neighbouring magnetic nuclei in the molecule. These splittings provide informa-

Below: a nuclear magnetic resonance spectrometer. The pen recorder plots the resonant frequencies of the sample, and from these the analyst can determine its chemical composition.

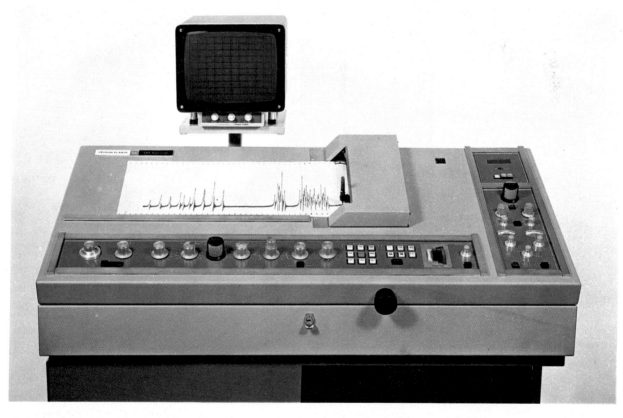

PERKIN-ELMER

tion about the number and disposition of the neighbouring nuclei. The range of absorption frequencies is small for each isotope, hydrogen for example having a total spread of a few kilohertz at a resonance frequency of 100 megahertz. The signal splittings are much smaller, less than one hertz in some cases, and their measurement requires elaborate instrumentation.

NMR spectrometers The instrument used for these measurements is an NMR spectrometer. This consists of a magnet, a radio frequency source and detector, and an arrangement for sweeping the spectrum, by varying either the magnetic field strength or the frequency. To obtain the maximum separation between signals it is desirable to use as strong a magnetic field as possible. Both permanent and electromagnets are used with field strengths in the range 14 to 23 kilogauss, the corresponding resonance frequencies for hydrogen being 60 to 100 MHz. To obtain even higher field strengths SUPERCONDUCTING solenoids are used, with possible field strengths up to 80 kilogauss.

The magnetic field has to be extremely uniform as any variation leads to broadening of the observed signals. The sample is usually contained in a glass tube 0.2 to 0.4 inch (5 to 10 mm) in diameter and the magnetic field across this must vary by less than one part in 100,000,000. To achieve this the magnet is fitted with a series of correcting coils which generate magnetic fields to cancel out inhomogeneity (unevenness) in the original field. In addition the field must be very stable so that the relative positions of signals can be measured accurately.

With permanent magnets it is possible to stabilize the field by controlling the magnet temperature very precisely, but this cannot be done with electromagnets because of the heat dissipated. Instead a reference NMR signal is used with a FEEDBACK system to keep constant the resonance frequency, and hence the magnetic field. To scan the spectrum either the radio frequency or the magnetic field can be varied. A recent alternative is to irradiate the sample with a broad band of frequencies and to use an on-line computer to analyse the response of the sample.

Most applications involve the study of organic compounds through their hydrogen resonance. Although the range of absorption frequencies is small, the relative positions are highly characteristic of the immediate surroundings of the hydrogen atom in the molecule. The splittings seen in each signal can identify the number of hydrogen nuclei near to those giving the signal and also the number and orientation of the chemical bonds separating them. The hydrogen spectrum can be used to map out the location of the hydrogen atoms in the molecule, and so determine the molecular structure.

The main limitation of the method is that different signals often overlap, so that less information can be obtained. To overcome this, stronger magnetic fields are constantly being developed. The spectrum obtained from the carbon-13 nuclei often complements the hydrogen spectrum, and although it is more difficult to measure because the signals are very weak, the use of computer techniques has enabled carbon resonance to become a useful method.

Below: a simplified diagram of an NMR spectrometer. The sample, in a glass tube, is placed between the poles of an extremely strong magnet, adjacent to the radio frequency source coils and the sweep coils. The signals from the sample are picked up by a detector coil surrounding the tube, amplified, and fed to the recorder.

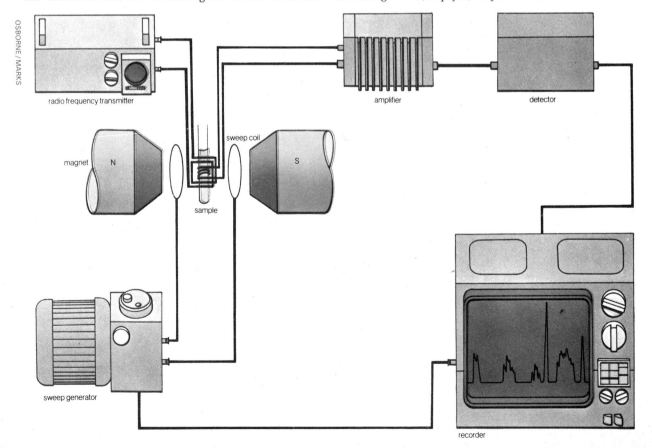

OSBORNE / MARKS

radio frequency transmitter

amplifier

detector

magnet N

sweep coil

S

sample

sweep generator

recorder

NUCLEAR REACTOR

The discovery of RADIOACTIVITY in 1896 revealed that the elements thorium and URANIUM release ENERGY spontaneously. The release accompanies a series of radioactive transformations in which ATOMS emit particles or rays and change their chemical identity. The rate of energy release is too slow to be of much practical use and it seemed that nothing could be done to hasten it.

A breakthrough occurred in 1919, when RUTHERFORD discovered that *alpha-rays* could shatter the atomic NUCLEUS. Further research led to the discovery of the NEUTRON in 1932 and of the FISSION of uranium in 1939. That year it became clear that a nuclear CHAIN REACTION could probably be set up, using uranium, and that this might be the means, not only of releasing vast amounts of energy, but also of producing a new element, *plutonium*. There was the possibility that an A-BOMB could be developed and it was to produce plutonium for such a bomb that the Hanford Works was built beside the Columbia River in the USA. Here, the world's first industrial-scale nuclear reactor for the production of plutonium commenced operation in 1944.

At Hanford, the heat of the nuclear reaction was carried away by river water. The next step was to develop reactors whose heat could be converted into useful power. This meant higher operating temperatures.

In the USA, the first objective was SUBMARINE propulsion, the USS *Nautilus* commencing sea trials in 1955. In Britain, Calder Hall was being built, for the dual purposes of plutonium production and electricity generation, and a programme of nuclear power was put before Parliament. In the USSR, an atomic power plant had commenced operation at Obninsk in 1954. Twenty years later, nearly 250 sea-going nuclear propulsion plants and about 120 full-scale industrial nuclear power reactors were in operation by 16 nations.

When a nuclear reactor is operating, neutrons are emitted and absorbed by the fuel, while heat is released in it. As the nuclear fuel 'burns', its nature gradually changes.

The neutron is a nuclear particle which has no electric charge. It can penetrate matter, only occasionally colliding with an atomic nucleus, rather as one might walk blindfold in an orchard, occasionally bumping into a tree trunk. When a collision occurs, the neutron either bounces off in a new direction, or is captured, forming a *compound nucleus*.

Thermal reactor Generally speaking, the chances that a neutron will interact with a nucleus are much higher when the neutron's velocity is low than when it is moving fast. For this reason, in the so-called *thermal reactors*, a *moderator* is used to slow down the neutrons emitted by the fuel to the velocities of thermal agitation. The slowing down occurs because the neutrons lose their energy of motion to the *moderating* nuclei, as they bounce off them .The energy transfer is more effective the lighter these nuclei. The most commonly used moderators are graphite, a form of carbon (nuclear mass approximately twelve times that of the neutron), and ordinary or 'light' water, which contains hydrogen (mass approximately equal to that of the neutron). Light water is the most effective at slowing neutrons, but captures most.

Above left: the top of the core of a High Flux Isotope Reactor. The blue glow in the water surrounding the core is Cerenkov radiation, which occurs when charged particles pass through the water at a speed greater than the speed of light in water.
Left: Cerenkov radiation from fuel elements in a storage pool.

UKAEA

The consequences of neutron capture are different for different types of nucleus. The nuclei of naturally occurring uranium atoms are of two types or ISOTOPES, containing different numbers of particles. 99.3% have 238 particles, but 0.7% have 235. It is the existence of uranium-235 that has made possible the nuclear reactor.

When a neutron is captured by uranium-235, the resulting compound nucleus, uranium-236, may remain intact, but is more likely to undergo fission, splitting into two fission product nuclei of approximately equal mass, and emitting fast-moving neutrons. Because it is so likely to undergo fission, uranium-235 is called a *fissile* material.

Capture of a neutron by uranium-238 yields, as compound nucleus, uranium-239. This does not split, but it undergoes spontaneous radioactive transformations, increasing the positive electric charge of its nucleus by emitting two *beta-rays* and so becoming plutonium-239. This nucleus, an isotope of the second element beyond uranium in the PERIODIC TABLE, is fissile. Because it can be converted into a fissile material, uranium-238 is said to be a *fertile* material. In nuclear reactors, both fissile and fertile materials have important parts to play.

A chain reaction of nuclear fission proceeds steadily if, on average, one of the two or three neutrons emitted in each fission triggers off a further fission. This leaves one or two spare neutrons per fission. In a nuclear reactor, some of these spare neutrons are deliberately absorbed in 'control rods', partially inserted into the moderator. Others are unavoidably lost by capture in uranium-235 not followed by fission, by capture in the moderator, coolant, fission fragments and structural materials and by leakage from the reactor. The rest may profitably be absorbed in the fertile material, so producing

Top right: schematic view of a nuclear reactor. Fast neutrons produced by the fissile fuel are slowed down in the moderator and then can be reabsorbed to initiate further fission. Neutron-absorbing rods are raised and lowered to control the speed of the reaction.

Above: the aluminium clad containment building of the Advanced Gas-Cooled Reactor (AGR) at Windscale, England. The gas-cooled graphite moderated reactor is fuelled with uranium oxide in stainless steel cans which permit very high operating temperatures.

new fissile material.

Some thermal reactors are fuelled with uranium of natural isotopic composition, but, for the majority, the uranium is first put through an isotope separation process, to remove some of the uranium-238. The use of this 'enriched' uranium, usually with between 2 and 4% uranium-235 content, gives greater freedom in reactor design.

In practice, the ratio of the number of plutonium-239 nuclei produced to the number of uranium-235 nuclei consumed, in a thermal reactor, is less than one. If the plutonium is required for A-bomb manufacture, the fuel may be discharged at an early stage. Otherwise, it is left in the reactor for a period of between three and five years, during which some of the plutonium-239 is burnt up by fission and some is converted to higher isotopes, plutonium-240, -241 and -242. Of these, only plutonium-241 is fissile.

Thorium Despite the conversion of some uranium-238 into plutonium, thermal reactors cannot, on their own, afford a prospect of being able to burn up by fission more than about 2% of a stock of natural uranium. It is with the objective of improving the utilization of potential nuclear fuels that two

OSBORNE / MARKS

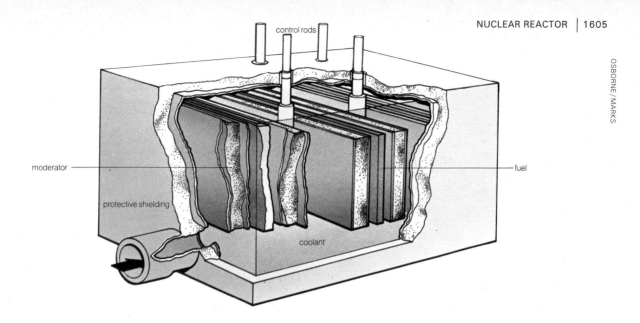

control rods

moderator

protective shielding

fuel

coolant

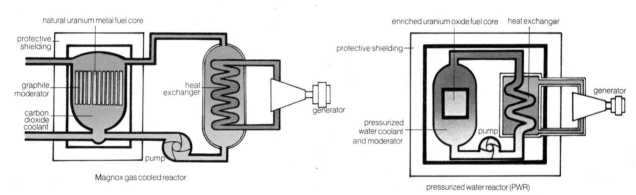

natural uranium metal fuel core

protective shielding

graphite moderator

carbon dioxide coolant

heat exchanger

generator

pump

Magnox gas cooled reactor

enriched uranium oxide fuel core

heat exchanger

protective shielding

pressurized water coolant and moderator

generator

pump

pressurized water reactor (PWR)

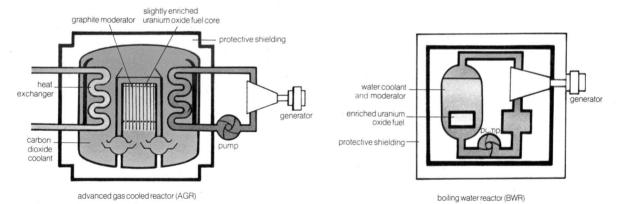

graphite moderator

slightly enriched uranium oxide fuel core

protective shielding

heat exchanger

generator

carbon dioxide coolant

pump

advanced gas cooled reactor (AGR)

water coolant and moderator

enriched uranium oxide fuel

protective shielding

generator

pump

boiling water reactor (BWR)

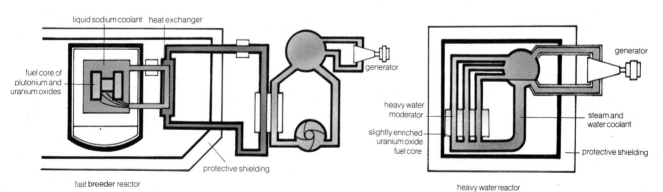

liquid sodium coolant

heat exchanger

fuel core of plutonium and uranium oxides

generator

protective shielding

fast **breeder** reactor

generator

heavy water moderator

slightly enriched uranium oxide fuel core

steam and water coolant

protective shielding

heavy water reactor

further lines of nuclear reactor development are being pursued. One scheme is to substitute thorium, which has only one naturally occurring isotope, thorium-232, for uranium-238 as fertile material. This would result in the production of the fissile material uranium-233. The properties of this nucleus are better suited to thermal reactor operation than are those of plutonium-239 and it is believed that its use would make it possible to burn up a high percentage of a stock of thorium.

Fast breeder reactor

The other line of development is the *fast breeder reactor*, which uses plutonium isotopes as fissile material and uranium-238 as fertile material, with no moderator. Operating with fast neutrons, the properties of plutonium are better, there being less tendency for it to be converted into non-fissile isotopes. The result is that more than one nucleus of uranium can be converted into plutonium-239 for each plutonium nucleus destroyed, so that the initial stock of plutonium grows or 'breeds'. The important point is that fast breeder reactors should afford the means of obtaining very much more energy from the world's uranium reserves than would be possible with thermal reactors alone.

An atomic nucleus is positively charged. When it is undergoing fission, the two parts separate until the forces of attraction associated with BINDING ENERGY cease to be effective. The two parts, each of which carries about half of the charge, are then driven apart at great speed by ELECTROSTATIC repulsion.

The major part of the energy released in fission initially takes the form of this energy of motion of the fission products. As these are brought to rest in the surrounding fuel, the energy becomes distributed, appearing as heat. There is a further liberation of heat as the fission products, which form atoms of about 30 different elements, undergo radioactive transformations.

Fuel elements

In some reactors, the fuel is uranium metal, but uranium oxide and carbide stand up better to high temperatures and to the accumulation of fission products. Rods or pellets of fuel are sealed into thin-walled metal tubes which, in some designs, are grouped into clusters of 36 to form a *fuel element*. For the highest temperatures, graphite is used instead of metal for cladding the fuel.

The fuel elements, in general, are held in vertical channels through which flow streams of coolant. The most commonly used coolants are the gases carbon dioxide or helium, water, either 'light' or *heavy* (containing atoms of the hydrogen isotope *deuterium* rather than normal hydrogen), and molten sodium metal. When water is used, it is either held under such high pressure that it remains in liquid form at a temperature

Below left: checking the fuel temperature thermocouples in the top of the reactor pile of the AGR at Windscale. The thermocouples monitor the temperature of the fuel elements in the reactor.

UKAEA

far above the normal boiling point, or else the pressure is adjusted so that steam generation occurs as the water is passing over the fuel elements. In the latter case, the steam passes direct from reactor to TURBINE. Otherwise, the coolant goes to a HEAT EXCHANGER, where it gives up heat to a secondary stream of water, which turns to steam.

Whichever coolant is used, it must be kept under pressure. This is usually done by enclosing the fuel, moderator and coolant in a pressure vessel, but an alternative is to place fuel and coolant only in an array of pressure tubes with the moderator outside. In all reactors, a concrete *biological shield* several feet thick protects people in the vicinity from radiation.

Nuclear waste

Eventually, mainly because of the deleterious effects of the accumulating *fission products*, the fuel must be discharged from the reactor. It is next allowed to 'cool' for some months, to let much of the radioactivity die away, and is then transported in heavily shielded 'flasks' to a reprocessing plant, such as the Windscale Works of British Nuclear Fuels Limited. Here, the residual uranium and plutonium are extracted by chemical separation.

Of the fission products, krypton and xenon isotopes are released to atmosphere during reprocessing. Small quantities of other fission products, dispersed in large quantities of water, may be discharged into the sea or, if the reprocessing plant is inland, pumped into the ground. Apart from these, the fission products are stored in jacketed stainless steel tanks, placed in thick-walled concrete 'cells'. Among proposals for the ultimate disposal of these wastes is their incorporation into highly insoluble glassy substances and their entombment in carefully chosen geological formations.

Future applications

Looking to the future, nuclear reactors are expected to be the means of meeting much of the world's growing demand for electricity. Nuclear reactors are also likely to be used to supply heat for industrial processes. Steel-making, DESALINATION of sea water and producing substitutes for petroleum fuels are among the probable future applications. Nuclear propulsion of large merchant ships, already demonstrated in the American *Savannah* and the West German *Otto Hahn*, is expected to become economic. Nuclear reactors will probably be used for electricity supplies in space and may possibly serve for propulsion of long-range manned missions to explore the planets.

Below left: the underside of a machine which inserts fuel elements into the Prototype Fast Reactor at Dounreay, Scotland, which is now producing 250 MW of electricity for northern Scotland.

Below: a handling flask for irradiated fuel for the Dragon reactor at Winfrith, England. Dragon is an experimental high temperature, helium cooled, graphite moderated reactor.

NUCLEUS

The nucleus is the tiny core of the ATOM where almost all the mass is concentrated. It is built up of PROTONS and NEUTRONS packed together in a volume about a million millionth of a centimetre across, while the atom's ELECTRON cloud spreads out ten thousand times wider.

The number of protons and neutrons in nuclei can vary between one (the single proton at the centre of the HYDROGEN atom) and about 250 (for example, a mixture of 100 protons and 150 neutrons at the centre of the *fermium* atom). It is the number of protons, equivalent to the number of surrounding electrons, which dictates the type of chemical element, while the number of neutrons grouped with a given number of protons produces several ISOTOPES of the same element. In general the number of neutrons is in excess of the number of protons and the excess is greater in the heavier elements.

Some nuclei are extremely stable. An example is the LEAD nucleus with 82 protons and 126 neutrons; such numbers (and others) became known as 'magic' numbers because the way in which they produce such high stability is not fully understood. Other nuclei are unstable (or radioactive). This is particularly true of the heavy nuclei such as *plutonium*. They tend to break up either by emitting clumps of two protons and two neutrons (alpha decay) or by emitting electrons as neutrons break up (beta decay). In rare instances, they FISSION into two approximately equal halves.

The discovery that protons and neutrons can cluster together in nuclei was one of the most important ever made in physics because it led to the discovery of a new force operating in Nature. In the early 1930s, there was no understanding of how positively charged protons could stay so close to one another without repelling, like similar poles of magnets, or of how

neutrons, with no charge at all, could be held. In 1935, a Japanese physicist, H Yukawa, developed the theory that a previously unknown force is in action in the nucleus. It is called the 'strong force' since it is much more powerful than the electrical force which is tending to push the protons apart.

The force operates by the exchange of light particles, known as *pions*, between the protons and neutrons. These pions cannot be seen when looking at the behaviour of the nucleus as a whole but emerge in large quantities when a nucleus is hit by a high energy particle from an accelerator. The nucleus can be compared to a group of ball players viewed from a distance. It is not obvious that they are clustered close together because they are exchanging a ball from one to another unless the group is broken up and the ball emerges by itself. The exchange of pions can go on over only very short distances, which explains why the nucleus is packed so close and why the strong force does not pull in other protons or neutrons from the outskirts of an atom but only captures them when they penetrate the nuclear volume itself.

Knowledge of the major features of the nucleus has made it possible to tap the strong force as a source of energy and to bring nuclear power into the service of mankind.

NYLON MANUFACTURE (see fibre, synthetic)

Below: most elements have spherical nuclei, but some heavier nuclei are elongated. Two unusual shapes are shown here: those of yttrium (like a flattened disc with projections from the centre of each side) and samarium (like a double doughnut). Both are stable nuclei. This was discovered by 'elastic scattering'—bombardment with alpha particles, which are deflected in various directions by large nuclei, giving an indication of the shape of the object they are hitting.

OSBORNE/MARKS

Below right: physicists have tried to find reasons why the nuclei of some elements are more stable than those of others, and also to build up a system of 'magic numbers' of particles in the nucleus, similar to the numbers of electrons in atoms which make elements stable, and therefore inert, as described in the article on the periodic table. This graph shows the neutron absorption (σ_t) of nuclei with an even number of protons (even Z, or atomic number). The horizontal scale shows the mean (average) number of neutrons in the nucleus ($\overline{N}$). The 'magic numbers', represented by low points in the value of σ_t, fall at 28, 50, 80 and 126. For example, lead (Pb), with a mean neutron number of 126 and atomic number of 50, has ten stable isotopes, more than any other element. Many radioactive elements finally decay to lead. Graphs of other characteristics show similar 'magic numbers'.

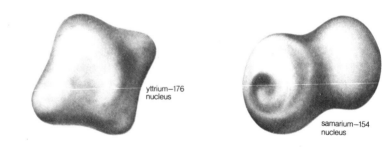

yttrium—176 nucleus

samarium—154 nucleus

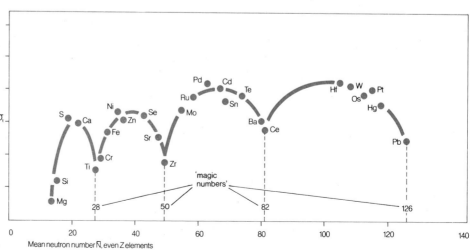

OBSERVATORY

The word 'observatory' can refer to any place where some kind of physical phenomenon is measured—hence geophysical and tidal observatories—but the term is usually reserved for astronomical observatories. For the best results, the site and buildings of an observatory have to be decided upon with care.

The early astronomers would observe from convenient sites near their homes—William HERSCHEL discovered the planet Uranus from his back garden, for example—and in the nineteenth century it became common for universities to have their own observatory, usually sited on the campus. But at the end of that century, as larger telescopes were built and city populations grew, it became obvious that sites well away from cities had advantages. While some large observatories are still situated near sea level, it has become increasingly common to site large ASTRONOMICAL TELESCOPES on top of very high mountains, leaving the city observatories for educational and public use.

Atmospheric pollution tends to be confined to the lower levels of the atmosphere. Another major factor affecting the quality of observations is the *seeing*—generally speaking, the

Above: the solar telescope at Kitt Peak, also shown overleaf. Other telescopes at Kitt Peak include a 158 inch (4 metre) reflector. Below: one of the world's major new observatories, the European Southern Observatory, under construction at La Silla in Chile. This is run by a consortium of European countries, and offers observing conditions considerably better than anywhere in Europe.

OSBORNE / MARKS

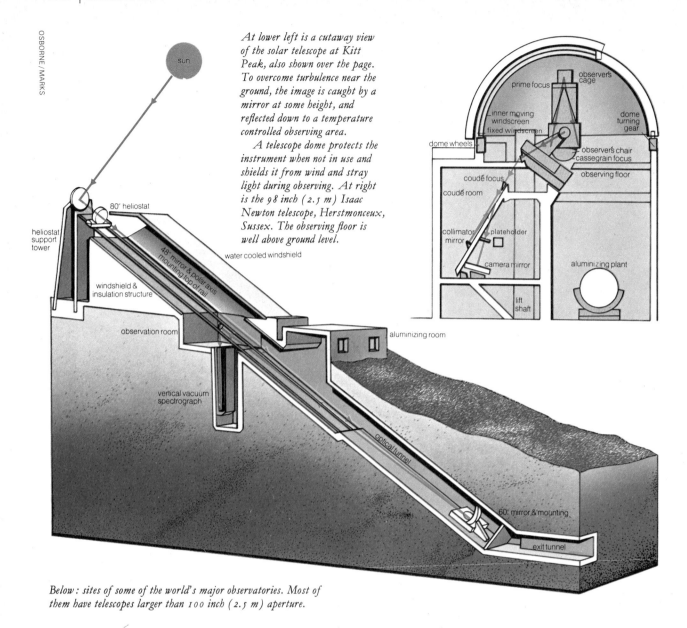

sun

80° heliostat

heliostat support tower

windshield & insulation structure

48° mirror & polar axis mounting top of rail

water cooled windshield

observation room

vertical vacuum spectrograph

aluminizing room

optical tunnel

60° mirror & mounting

exit tunnel

At lower left is a cutaway view of the solar telescope at Kitt Peak, also shown over the page. To overcome turbulence near the ground, the image is caught by a mirror at some height, and reflected down to a temperature controlled observing area.

A telescope dome protects the instrument when not in use and shields it from wind and stray light during observing. At right is the 98 inch (2.5 m) Isaac Newton telescope, Herstmonceux, Sussex. The observing floor is well above ground level.

prime focus

observers cage

inner moving windscreen

fixed windscreen

dome turning gear

dome wheels

observers chair

cassegrain focus

observing floor

coudé focus

coudé room

collimator mirror

plateholder

camera mirror

aluminizing plant

lift shaft

Below: sites of some of the world's major observatories. Most of them have telescopes larger than 100 inch (2.5 m) aperture.

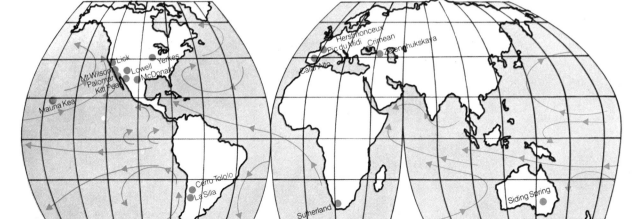

Lick

Yerkes

Mt Wilson

Lowell

Palomar

McDonald

Kitt Peak

Mauna Kea

Cerro Tololo

La Silla

Herstmonceux

Pic du Midi

Crimean

Zelenchukskaya

Calar Alto

Sutherland

Siding Spring

amount of air turbulence between the telescope and the object under observation. Under conditions of poor seeing, the image of a star as seen through a large telescope is no longer a point of light but is a rapidly wobbling blur, sometimes appearing to explode, to reappear a few instants later a short distance away. Poor seeing can be caused by high level winds, but a common cause is the turbulence quite close to the telescope. Cities, with their uneven surfaces and heated buildings, have very disturbed air above them even on still, cool days when there is no apparent heating by the sun. A mountain site therefore lifts the telescopes above nearby sources of turbulence. Dry, low humidity, air is also desirable.

Choosing a site

Many mountain or hilly areas suffer from generally poor weather conditions. Considerable research is therefore necessary, these days on a worldwide scale, to find sites which get good weather for a sufficient proportion of the time to make it worthwhile setting up an observatory. Normal clear weather conditions, however, result in the sun heating the lower levels of the atmosphere, creating large scale turbulence; on encountering a mountain range, the rising air mass cools and its water vapour content condenses into clouds. The ideal conditions are those where there is a *temperature inversion*; that is, where for some reason cold air is trapped below a warmer layer of air. This occurs at the western edges of continents where there is a stable anti-cyclone over the ocean (see METEOROLOGY)—notably along the coasts of California and Chile. The coastlines tend to be mist-shrouded, since there is usually a cold polar sea current. The inversion traps the moisture and pollution, and above it are found very clear, dry conditions.

The observatories built in the first half of this century in California at, for example, Mt Hamilton and Mt Palomar, enjoy excellent seeing conditions and good weather for this reason. More recently, observatories have been set up in the foothills of the Andes which many believe offer the best seeing conditions in the world. These observatories, such as those at Cerro Tololo and La Silla, both at an altitude of 7875 feet (2400 m), and each with a telescope of about 150 inches (3.8 m) aperture, are frequently in calm conditions above a cloud layer. A new South African observatory at Sutherland, in the semi-desert of the Karroo, is in a similar climatic region.

Good observing conditions also occur where a solitary peak projects-into a stable air flow. This is the case at the Pic du Midi Observatory, just to the north of the French Pyrenees at an altitude of 9400 feet (2860 m), which is shielded from the prevailing winds by the main mountain chain, and at the extinct sea volcanoes of Mauna Kea in Hawaii, and Tenerife in the Canary Islands.

Buildings

Having decided upon a site which optimizes the various requirements, including accessibility and freedom from aircraft on regular airways, as much care must go into the design of the observatory buildings. The aim is to make the temperature inside the observatory dome, where the telescope is located, as close to the outside nighttime air temperature as possible; if the dome were heated, the hot air would rush out of the open slit creating very bad seeing conditions. As a result, domes are painted white to reflect sunlight during the day, and are usually well insulated so that the temperature inside the dome does not vary much from its nighttime value. A glass-walled visitor's area is often provided to prevent them from raising the temperature. Although the air temperature could be equalized fairly rapidly, the telescope and its optics would take longer to cool down and the focus point would slowly change while this happened.

Below : one attempt to improve observing conditions was the Stratoscope balloon-borne telescope. In 1970 it reached an altitude of 80,000 feet (24 km) and photographed planets and galaxies.

OERSTED, Hans Christian (1777–1851)

A central theme of 19th century physics was the unification of previously separate branches of PHYSICS. In 1820 Hans Christian Oersted made one of the earliest and most significant discoveries in this respect when he found a connection between ELECTRICITY and magnetism (see ELECTROMAGNETISM).

The son of a poor apothecary, Oersted grew up in the small, remote town of Rudkjöbing, which is on the Danish island of Langeland. There he and his younger brother conducted an extraordinary self-education programme which, with only slight tutorial assistance, took them all the way to entrance at the University of Copenhagen in 1794. Oersted's brother eventually gained great eminence in the Danish legal profession, while Oersted himself turned to science and became Denmark's leading physicist.

Oersted's physical research was profoundly influenced by philosophical ideas. Having learned German as a boy, Oersted absorbed German philosophy and completed his doctoral dissertation on Kant's philosophy in 1799. While visiting Germany in 1801, he met, among others, Friedrich Wilhelm Joseph Schelling. Schelling taught that all the apparently separate powers of nature (such as electricity and magnetism) were, in reality, unified. Oersted accepted Schelling's general view of nature but came to place more importance than did Schelling on the necessity of empirically demonstrating the connections between nature's powers.

Oersted's desire for empirical evidence stemmed naturally from his scientific interests. In 1800 he took charge of an apothecary's shop and delivered lectures on chemistry. In the same year the announcement of Alessandro VOLTA's invention of a battery caught Oersted's attention and led to his own electrical researches. In 1806, at the age of 29, he became professor of physics at the University of Copenhagen. During many years of scientific research, Oersted frequently expressed his belief in the unity of nature's powers and continued searching for a connection between electricity and magnetism. In 1820 he found it. While delivering a lecture, Oersted brought a magnetic needle close to a wire carrying an electric current. The needle was deflected. Unlike other forces in nature already known, the force between the electric wire and the magnetic needle turned out to be a non-central force. Whereas a falling rock, for example, is attracted towards the centre of the Earth, Oersted's magnetic needle was not attracted towards the wire. No matter where it was placed in the vicinity of the wire, it pointed perpendicular to the wire. This indicated the presence of a force encircling the wire.

When Oersted sent word of his results throughout Europe a few months after his initial discovery, he caused a sensation and prompted a whole new line of scientific research. Attacking problems posed by Oersted's discovery, physicists found many other connections between electricity and magnetism and formulated far-reaching theories to explain them. Especially important were the researches of André Marie AMPÈRE in France and Michael FARADAY in England.

Although primarily known for this one discovery, Oersted did research in other areas as well—most importantly on the compressibility of water. Also, his literary and political interests made him a figure of some note in the broader areas of Danish intellectual life.

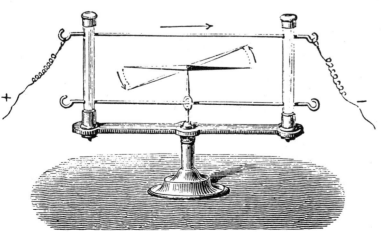

Above: an engraving of Hans Christian Oersted. He seems to be holding a piece of aluminium, a recently discovered element of which he made the first pure sample in 1825. On the table is a compass needle, commemorating his famous experiment of 1819.

Left: the 1819 experiment. Current passing through the metal rod causes the compass needle to deflect at right angles to it.

OHM, Georg Simon (1787–1854)

Although ELECTRICITY had been known and studied for centuries, an electric current was not produced until 1800 (by Alessandro VOLTA) when Georg Simon Ohm was 13 years old. It was in this new and exciting area of PHYSICS that Ohm discovered the fundamental law which bears his name.

Ohm, who was the son of a prosperous locksmith, grew up in Erlangen, Bavaria. His father had found his own knowledge of mathematics helpful and decided that Ohm and his brother should also study mathematics before joining the family business. Accordingly, when they finished elementary school, they entered the *Gymnasium* (secondary school) in Erlangen. Their mathematical successes there brought them to the attention of Karl Christian von Langsdorf, professor at the University of Erlangen. Langsdorf's proclamation of the brothers' genius launched them into scientific careers.

In 1805 Ohm entered the University of Erlangen. During the next few years he spent periods at the University of Erlangen and also held a series of teaching posts elsewhere. Finally, in 1817 at the age of thirty, he found a secure position teaching mathematics and physics at the Cologne Gymnasium. Now his interest began to turn more and more towards original research, and in 1827 he published his principal work, *The Galvanic Circuit, Mathematically Treated*.

Ohm's main finding concerned the relationship between the voltage, resistance, and current in an electric circuit. Now known as Ohm's law (see CIRCUIT, electrical), the relationship can be written as $V = IR$, where I is the current in the circuit, V the voltage producing the current, and R the resistance of the circuit to the current. Hence, if the voltage is doubled, the current will be doubled; if the resistance is doubled, the current will be halved. The unit in which resistances are measured has been named the ohm. The inverse of the resistance is called the conductance (G), and the name of its unit is Ohm's name spelled backwards—the mho. This definition of conductance is expressed by the two equations: $G = 1/R$ and $I = GV$.

Ohm's law is an example of a frequent occurrence in the history of science—the discovery of a very simple correlation of phenomena which previously appeared erratic and complicated. For various reasons, however, Ohm's results were not immediately accepted. One reason was the prevalence in early 19th century Germany of the view that experimentation and mathematics were irrelevant to a true understanding of nature. For supporters of this view, Ohm's results were simply beside the point. Others took Ohm's results more seriously but, with the experimental apparatus available, had great difficulty in verifying them. Recognition eventually came to Ohm in the early 1840s from British scientists. The Royal Society of London awarded him its Copley Medal in 1841, and in 1843 the great British electrician Charles Wheatstone praised Ohm's work as having guided his own.

This foreign acclaim reversed Ohm's fortunes in Germany. From a man somewhat embittered by neglect, he became a man of high reputation for the last decade of his life. He spent these last years developing a molecular theory to explain virtually all physical phenomena, but the theory was far from complete when he died aged sixty-seven.

OHM'S LAW (see resistance)

Below left: portrait of Ohm wearing the Copley medal, won in 1841.

Below: reconstruction of Ohm's apparatus for 'galvanic analysis'—basically a current measuring device using a compass needle hanging on a thread. Current is supplied by heat-powered thermocouples to avoid the voltage variations of primitive batteries.

OIL EXPLORATION

Oilfields are sometimes pictured as pools of oil underground, but oil and gas are normally found trapped in the pores of rock. As well as this reservoir rock—usually sand, sandstone, limestone or dolomite—impermeable 'cap rock' must also be present in an oilfield, to prevent the oil migrating from the reservoir area. Oil exploration means, in the first place, finding large basins of reservoir rock, associated with geological structures that may have acted as cap rock in trapping any oil the sedimentary reservoir deposits may hold. Techniques for doing this have been outlined in GEOLOGICAL TECHNIQUES and GEOPHYSICS, and their application to oil exploration is discussed here.

When suitable geological structures are found, it may mean that oil is present, but the only way to find if it occurs in commercial amounts is to drill test wells. The cost of doing so is the greater part of the hundreds of millions of pounds that may be spent on exploration and development of a major oilfield before any oil is obtained from it.

Exploration starts with assessment of existing data, supplemented by geological studies of accessible strata. Fossils and associated material help to date and identify rocks. Very accurate measurements of age can be obtained by analysis of radio-isotopes (see ISOTOPES).

Except when applied to drillings or cores from test wells, these methods give information on structures that appear on the surface. What is really needed is a map of strata down to several kilometres underground, and much information for this can be obtained from geophysical exploration methods. The principal methods are magnetic and gravity surveys and, above all, seismic exploration. Only after the results of studies of this kind have been examined are the locations of test wells decided.

Magnetic methods

The Earth's magnetic field varies with position and with time, and also because of magnetic storms. Allowing for these effects, results can be used to locate sedimentary basins and to estimate their thickness. Sedimentary rocks are virtually non-magnetic but the rocks (both igneous and metamorphic) below the sedimentary level are magnetic to differing degrees, resulting in small distortions in the Earth's magnetic field. The degree of these distortions depends on the distance of the source from the detector and can therefore be used to measure thickness of the sedimentary formation. Results are not easy to interpret, but magnetic surveys have the advantage that they can be done rapidly and economically from an aircraft and, therefore, over water or any type of land.

A MAGNETOMETER is either mounted in the tail of an aircraft or, more usually, trailed behind. Sensitivity is such that it can measure a magnetic field to less than one gamma. The survey aircraft flies at constant altitude along a set pattern of flight lines while the magnetic readings are recorded continuously.

Gravity surveys

The Earth's gravity also varies from place to place and, again when allowances have been made for that, the very precise methods of gravity measurement now

Below : oil is formed from microscopic marine organisms which died and sank to the bottom of the water, becoming trapped beneath mud. Then assisted by the pressure of underground water the oil percolated through the overlying porous rocks until its progress was halted by impervious rock. Shown here are some of the oil traps formed by major Earth movements. It is the underground pressure of the water and gas that helps to force the oil upwards when a well is drilled.

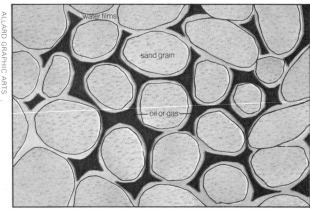

position of oil globules in reservoir rock

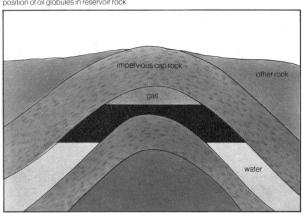

anticline trap

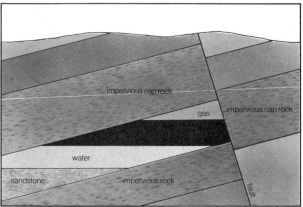

fault trap

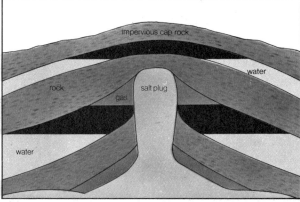

salt dome

available can be used to help locate sedimentary basins. Base rocks are denser and therefore have a higher gravity value than the sedimentary strata above and these differences can be measured with a gravimeter, which may be carried across land, be mounted on a gyroscopically stabilized platform on board a ship or even carried in an aircraft. Such a survey enables the sedimentary area to be defined.

Seismic methods Seismic methods (see SEISMOLOGY) provide information which is more precise. They depend on measuring the time that shock waves, produced by controlled explosions or in other ways, take to reflect or refract from rocks under the Earth's surface. Results of a large number of seismic tests can be correlated to give an accurate picture of the underground strata.

There are disadvantages in using explosions, though they are small and controlled, for seismic work, particularly for exploration at sea. Other methods use heavy weights falling, spark ignited gas explosions and powerful generators of specified frequency ranges.

Test wells Seismic results, taken with all the available data, allows selection of sites for test wells (see DRILLING RIG). Visual and electronic examination of drillings (the bits of broken rock flushed out with the drilling 'mud') during boring, supplemented with examination of rock 'cores', give much more information about the underground structure and the presence—or absence—of oil in commercial amounts. Electronic logging as the well is drilled also gives valuable information but, in spite of all the refined scientific methods used, there is still no certainty in oil exploration methods and the old saying that 'oil is where you find it' still sums up the uncertainty of locating it.

OIL REFINING

Crude oil, as it comes from the oil well, will always burn. But, except for some applications, such as operating a pump engine on a crude oil pipeline, it has to be refined to make it a satisfactory fuel. Also, it would be impossibly wasteful to burn crude oil, so losing many of its valuable constituents like chemicals feedstock, BITUMEN or lubricating oil.

Oil refining is therefore always necessary, and it does two main things to crude oil. It divides the crude into fractions of differing volatility, each with its own special application, and it alters some of these fractions physically or chemically either to make them more suitable for their own applications or to make it possible to use them for other applications where the demand is greater. For instance, crude oil can be divided into a gaseous fraction, and liquid fractions that form the basis of petrol [gasoline], paraffin [kerosene], diesel oil, fuel oil and, perhaps, bitumen or lubricating oil. For petrol [gasoline], however, the fraction produced by separation is not good enough in quality for a car engine to run on it and must be improved by refining processes. The crude oil may also not yield enough of the fraction in the right range to meet the demand, and other fractions of the yield may have to be altered so that they can be incorporated.

Refining, producing over 3000 million tons of products a year worldwide, is therefore a complex business. It is made more complex by the great variation of crude oil composition according to the area it comes from. Refineries must be able to produce the required balance of products from a range of crude oils and they must also be able to change the balance as demand changes. The change in demand may be relatively long term, as when vaporizing oil for tractors was replaced by

Below : a drilling rig for making seismic shot holes is mounted on a marsh buggy—a vehicle with large diameter, extra wide tyres, suitable for operating in sand. Right : an oil exploration camp in Saudi Arabia. Data from seismic and magnetic surveys will be collected here.

diesel oil, or it may be seasonal—for example, the demand for heating oil increases in the winter. Seasonal demands can to some extent be met by storage in the off-season, but refineries must arrange to make more of the product in demand at the expense of products less in demand. The scheduling needed to do this at maximum efficiency is so complicated that computers must be used to plan it.

Most refineries are built at deep water ports because they offer a number of advantages: large tankers can readily discharge crude oil to the refinery; the refined products can be transported cheaply by water to the markets; and ample cooling water is available for refining processes. A large refinery will require crude oil storage tank capacity of several hundred thousand tons, with some tanks taking up to 100,000 tons each, to accept full cargoes from modern large tankers.

Such a refinery may handle 20 million tons of crude oil in a year, and will represent an investment of hundreds of millions of pounds. As well as the plant for processing the crude oil, the refinery will need auxiliary services such as power and steam supply, and maintenance and laboratory facilities.

Even large refineries, however, do not need much manpower to operate them and an operating shift could consist of only about 25 people. The largest use of manpower is for maintenance teams, to keep refining plant in service and to maintain the complex automatic equipment and controls that keep a modern refinery in operation. AUTOMATIC CONTROL of processes is not primarily intended to save process manpower. It has developed to its present highly complex form—where just one refinery unit may have up to 200 automatic controls on it—because automation gives more efficient and safer operation

ESSO

Left: a large area of a refinery consists of tank farms where crude oil, intermediate and finished products are stored. Various process units can be seen in the centre. A vast network of pipes (perhaps as much as 1000 miles) connects the various areas. Products leave the refinery by road, rail, sea, or pipeline.

Below: typical refinery processes. The first step in refining is to split the crude oil into groups of compounds with similar boiling points. The amount of each fraction obtained depends on the particular crude oil. Sometimes the demand for certain products is greater than the natural yield so various conversion processes are necessary such as 'cracking' in which large molecules are broken into smaller ones, or polymerization whereby smaller molecules are built into larger ones. Most crude oils contain sulphur and desulphurization (hydrofining) is an important treatment.

than would be possible with greater manual operation supplemented by some automatic control. No modern refinery could be operated completely by manual controls, however many men stood by the valves and switches.

Refinery production A basic refinery might produce, from a limited range of crude oils, only petrol [gasoline], diesel oil and fuel oil. It would do this by separating the crude oil into fractions by DISTILLATION, and by appropriate treatment of the fractions intended for petrol by *catalytic reforming* (see below) of some of them and by *sweetening*.

A complex refinery would produce the same products, but would be able to do so from a much wider range of crude oils. The complex refinery would also produce liquefied petroleum gas (LPG), paraffin [kerosene], aviation fuel, bitumen and perhaps lubricating oils. United Kingdom refinery production

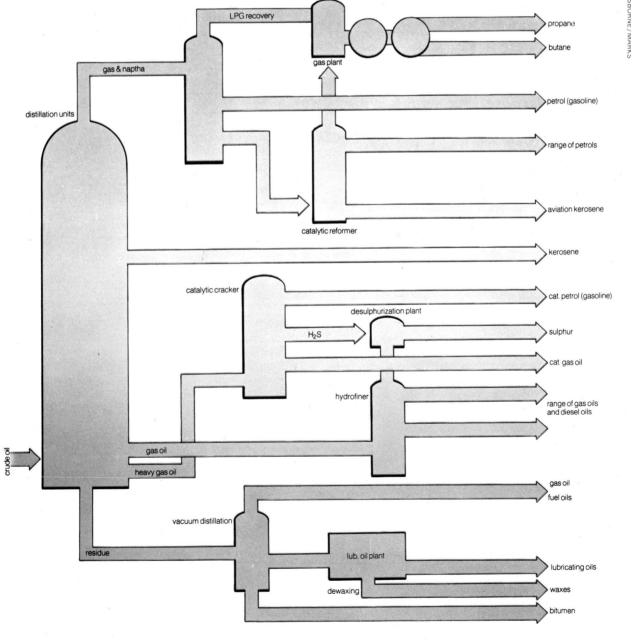

OSBORNE / MARKS

ON-LINE TERMINAL

A terminal, or data terminal to give it its correct name, is a COMPUTER peripheral (a machine used for the input, output, or storage of data) located at any point at which data may be the input to or output from a data communication system. Remote data transmission is the automatic transfer of data from one computer to another, or to and from a central computer and a distant terminal, the data being transferred by interface equipment using either telegraph or telephone lines, or in rare circumstances radio (MICROWAVE) links. The speed of transmission is to a great extent governed by the transmission line.

The simplest means of remote data transmission is by way of a paper TAPE READER connected by a standard telephone line to a paper tape punch at the computer centre. Data held on punched tape is read by a remote reader and transmitted to the punch, thereby producing an exact duplicate of the original punched tape. This technique is operated *off-line*, the resulting paper tape being fed into the computer by human operator. A terminal unit is provided at each end of the line to enable re-transmission in the event of errors. The next logical development in data transmission is to connect the line directly to the computer, so that the terminals can operate in an *on-line* mode, thereby doing away with the operator. This requires a program capable of handling such inputs since the remote terminal may commence transmitting at any time. This program must be able to maintain constant control over incoming data.

Modulation

To achieve efficient data transmission a *modem* is used. 'Modem' is an acronym for modulator-demodulator, a device which enables data to be transmitted over long distances without error.

Modulation is a technique used in radio, telegraphic and telephonic communications where data signals are used to modify either the amplitude or frequency of a carrier-wave. The carrier-wave is of a suitable frequency for transmitting over a transmission line, and when modulated carries with it the data signals which normally would not be capable of transmission. Demodulation is the converse of modulation (see AMPLITUDE MODULATION, FREQUENCY MODULATION, PULSE CODE MODULATION).

Multiplexing

Often there is a need for either a number of remote terminals requiring the services of a central computer, or a variety of remote terminals at one location. In these cases it is necessary to use a *multiplexer*, which enables a number of data terminals to communicate with the central computer.

Data from each terminal is fed via a standard interface into its respective transmission line. A typical multiplexer can scan many lines detecting the presence of a *data request*. If this exists, the scan is interrupted and the terminal's data line is switched to the data 'highway' connecting the multiplexer control to the central computer. The multiplexer will accept single characters of data passed over the transmission line in this way throughout the scanning sequence. Software which will assemble the characters into their individual messages is also required.

As an alternative to the multiplexer, several peripherals can be connected to a single remote terminal which transmits the information down a single transmission line. To achieve this each terminal is allocated a character 'address' which is used by the central computer to determine which peripheral is transmitting and which is receiving data. This technique is known as 'polling'.

Terminals for connection to transmission lines can be divided into those intended for batch processing and those for conversational work. Peripherals for batch processing work include paper-tape readers, paper-tape punches, card punches

Below: an on-line terminal comprising a typewriter unit and a paper tape unit.

Right: an on-line visual display terminal, a type of terminal which is widely used for such applications as airline seat reservation systems and banking systems.

Far right: Glasgow Fire Brigade is now using facsimile transmission terminals in its fire engines, so that information concerning a building can be sent to the engine on its way to a fire there.

BARCLAYS BANK LTD

BRITISH AIRWAYS

lesser amounts of heat and pressure in the presence of a CATALYST, which promotes the reaction without itself being permanently changed (*catalytic cracking*). Catalytic cracking is normally done by the *fluidized* technique: catalyst in fine granule form is made to move like a fluid through a reactor to a *regenerator*, where carbon that accumulates on it is burned off, and back through the cycle again. Catalytic cracking is normally used in making petrol [gasoline] and thermal cracking is particularly used in making chemicals feedstock. The cracking process gives MOLECULES that are better in anti-knock value as well as smaller.

Hydro-cracking adds hydrogen to the cracking process. Large quantities of hydrogen are produced in an integrated refinery. The effect is to provide more high quality petrol [gasoline] components, and to increase the versatility of the process.

Other processes   *Reforming* in one of the processes that produces hydrogen in the refinery, by removing it from naphthenes to give aromatics, which have much greater resistance to knocking. Other reactions, such as *isomerization* and *alkylation* are involved in reforming, and may be carried out separately. Isomerization changes straight chain compounds into branched chain ones, again greatly increasing resistance to

Left: a crude oil distillation unit which has a capacity of 160,000 barrels (25,458,000 litres) per day. This is the start of the refining process, where the crude oil is split into several different fractions depending on the boiling point range. Each fraction may then undergo other treatments such as desulphurization or cracking.

Below: a LPG (liquefied petroleum gas—butane or propane) tank. Butane can be liquefied at ambient temperature and moderate pressure.

knocking. For instance, *n*-hexane can be changed to 2-methyl pentane by isomerization, giving an increase in octane number (used to measure resistance to knocking) from 25 to 73 for just this change.

Other widely used physical processes include *solvent extraction,* which depends on one component of the fraction undergoing treatment being much more soluble in the solvent than in the remainder. This portion is carried away with the solvent and is later recovered from it. An example is the extraction of aromatics from paraffin [kerosene] with sulphur dioxide. If aromatics were left in the paraffin they would cause a smoky flame.

Lubricating oils   Only some crude oils have suitable constituents for making a range of lubricating oils. The residue from primary distillation is vacuum distilled to give oils of the right viscosity range. These are treated to remove unwanted compounds. Asphalt can be taken out by propane de-asphalting; aromatics, which would give poor viscosity-temperature characteristics, are removed by solvent extraction; and wax, which would stop the oil flowing at low temperatures, is removed by solvent de-waxing, providing a useful by-product.

Base oils made in this way are blended to give the right characteristics for particular applications and often have additives mixed with them to enhance specific properties.

Chemicals feedstock   An important refinery function is producing feedstock for chemical processes to give plastics, rubbers, solvents, and other petrochemicals. The chemical plants may be sited beside refineries or fed by PIPELINE over longer distances.

OIL RIG (see drilling rig)

ON-LINE TERMINAL

A terminal, or data terminal to give it its correct name, is a COMPUTER peripheral (a machine used for the input, output, or storage of data) located at any point at which data may be the input to or output from a data communication system. Remote data transmission is the automatic transfer of data from one computer to another, or to and from a central computer and a distant terminal, the data being transferred by interface equipment using either telegraph or telephone lines, or in rare circumstances radio (MICROWAVE) links. The speed of transmission is to a great extent governed by the transmission line.

The simplest means of remote data transmission is by way of a paper TAPE READER connected by a standard telephone line to a paper tape punch at the computer centre. Data held on punched tape is read by a remote reader and transmitted to the punch, thereby producing an exact duplicate of the original punched tape. This technique is operated *off-line*, the resulting paper tape being fed into the computer by human operator. A terminal unit is provided at each end of the line to enable re-transmission in the event of errors. The next logical development in data transmission is to connect the line directly to the computer, so that the terminals can operate in an *on-line* mode, thereby doing away with the operator. This requires a program capable of handling such inputs since the remote terminal may commence transmitting at any time. This program must be able to maintain constant control over incoming data.

Modulation To achieve efficient data transmission a *modem* is used. 'Modem' is an acronym for modulator-de-modulator, a device which enables data to be transmitted over long distances without error.

Modulation is a technique used in radio, telegraphic and telephonic communications where data signals are used to modify either the amplitude or frequency of a carrier-wave. The carrier-wave is of a suitable frequency for transmitting over a transmission line, and when modulated carries with it the data signals which normally would not be capable of transmission. Demodulation is the converse of modulation (see AMPLITUDE MODULATION, FREQUENCY MODULATION, PULSE CODE MODULATION).

Multiplexing Often there is a need for either a number of remote terminals requiring the services of a central computer, or a variety of remote terminals at one location. In these cases it is necessary to use a *multiplexer*, which enables a number of data terminals to communicate with the central computer.

Data from each terminal is fed via a standard interface into its respective transmission line. A typical multiplexer can scan many lines detecting the presence of a *data request*. If this exists, the scan is interrupted and the terminal's data line is switched to the data 'highway' connecting the multiplexer control to the central computer. The multiplexer will accept single characters of data passed over the transmission line in this way throughout the scanning sequence. Software which will assemble the characters into their individual messages is also required.

As an alternative to the multiplexer, several peripherals can be connected to a single remote terminal which transmits the information down a single transmission line. To achieve this each terminal is allocated a character 'address' which is used by the central computer to determine which peripheral is transmitting and which is receiving data. This technique is known as 'polling'.

Terminals for connection to transmission lines can be divided into those intended for batch processing and those for conversational work. Peripherals for batch processing work include paper-tape readers, paper-tape punches, card punches

Below: an on-line terminal comprising a typewriter unit and a paper tape unit.

Right: an on-line visual display terminal, a type of terminal which is widely used for such applications as airline seat reservation systems and banking systems.

Far right: Glasgow Fire Brigade is now using facsimile transmission terminals in its fire engines, so that information concerning a building can be sent to the engine on its way to a fire there.

BRITISH AIRWAYS

BARCLAYS BANK LTD

and readers (see CARD HANDLING MACHINES), LINEPRINTERS and graph plotters. Those for conversational computing include TYPEWRITER terminals and GRAPHIC DISPLAY units. It is these *interactive* devices which offer the most scope for developments in man-machine communication.

Software Computer manufacturers have software available to cover most of the needs of data communication. Basic software such as *executive routines* for batch processing and programs for on-line conversational work are very important. Within executive routines, facilities must be provided to enable a number of remote users to access the central computer in such a way that it seems as if each user has the entire facilities of the central computer at his disposal. On-line conversational software has been developed for specific areas of processing, such as simple mathematical calculation, to enable the remote user to have an immediate answer to his problem at any time he wishes.

Data communication is still in its infancy and as more facilities are introduced more and more computer users will be able to take advantage of 'instant processing'. Data communication is possible for the whole of industry and commerce in two ways. First, there are the companies who own large computers and who can establish data links with branch offices throughout the country. Secondly, there are the small companies who infrequently need fast answers to their problems. These companies will be able to benefit from the remote data transmission facilities being introduced by the larger computer bureaux.

In the future it is expected that a complex of data communications networks will be established in many countries and possibly linked together to form a world-wide network. These networks will enable many classes of remote terminal users to access powerful computers capable of handling almost every conceivable aspect of computer processing.

OPHTHALMOSCOPE

The ophthalmoscope is an optical device used for examining the interior of the eye. The pupil is the tiny black 'window' of the eye; through it we can view a wide landscape, but no one could look in from the outside until the ophthalmoscope was invented.

It was believed that the blackness of the pupil was due to the total absorption of light rays by the eye, but Herman von Helmholtz (1821–1894) discovered that most of the light entering the eye is reflected back and can be intercepted by an observer. Helmholtz was a physician and physicist who investigated the conservation of energy, the speed of nervous impulses, colour blindness, physiological acoustics and other subjects, but is most famous for his *Handbook of Physiological Optics* (1856–1866; complete edition 1867). In 1851 he hit upon the idea of directing a beam of light into the eye by means of a mirror in which there was a tiny aperture through which an observer could look.

For diagnostic purposes it is important to obtain a good view of the *fundus,* that part of the cavity of the eye which can be examined by looking through the pupil. This enables the observer to detect abnormalities and pathological changes in the eye; some diseases, such as diabetes, manifest themselves in the eye before symptoms appear elsewhere. The fundus, however, cannot be examined by a perforated mirror alone; this only gives a red reflex. Helmholtz found it was necessary to interpose a condenser LENS, with about a four inch (10 cm) focal length in order to obtain an inverted image, magnified five times. This combination of mirror and hand-held condenser was called an indirect ophthalmoscope and was in regular use for eye examinations until about 1920.

Nowadays ophthalmoscopy is carried out by a direct method with a hand-held instrument. From a tiny lamp powered by dry batteries which are located in the handle of the instrument, a narrow beam of light is directed through the pupil and into the eye of the patient by means of a prism or a perforated mirror of steel or glass. The image, magnified fifteen times, is viewed through the sight hole in the mirror and brought into focus by a revolving magazine of lenses, rotated by the index

Below: a doctor examining the eye of a patient using a hand-held ophthalmoscope. The instrument has batteries in the handle which power a tiny lamp. A narrow beam of light is directed through the pupil and into the eye.

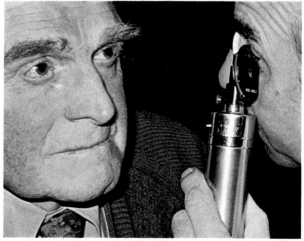

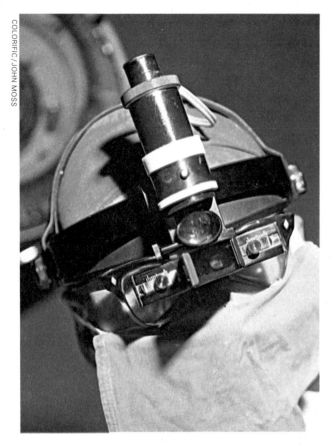

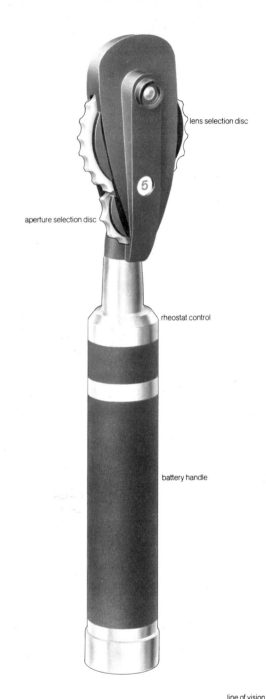

lens selection disc

aperture selection disc

rheostat control

battery handle

Above: patient's eye view of the doctor using a binocular ophthalmoscope. Also called indirect ophthalmoscopy because it uses mirrors and results in an inverted image, the binocular system provides a three-dimensional image.

Right: this ophthalmoscope uses a mirror instead of a prism for light transmission, which means that the viewing axis and the axis of the projection of the light are brought close to coincidence, making it easier to direct the light into a small or undilated pupil. The lamp has an orientated filament, and the rheostat adjusts the brightness of the light. Selection of lenses and apertures can be made by the doctor with one finger without having to move the instrument during an examination.

finger of the observer. It is interesting that the power required to focus the image represents the refractive error of the eye, and gives roughly the power of the spectacle lens required to correct the vision, but this is incidental to the real function of the instrument, which is the examination of the interior of the eye in order to detect abnormalities.

Many instruments are fitted with a variety of FILTERS, such as red-free and polarizing screens, which show up conditions not visible with white light. Cross line graticules can be projected on to the retina so that a particular point can be given a grid reference. There is also a new type of ophthalmoscope which projects a LASER beam; this is used in eye surgery to coagulate the tissue around a detached retina. For clinical research and a more detailed study of the eye, there is a large binocular ophthalmoscope which stands on an instrument table. With this it is possible to obtain a large stereoscopic picture of the fundus magnified about fifteen times.

slit

pin hole

clear

white line grid

red free

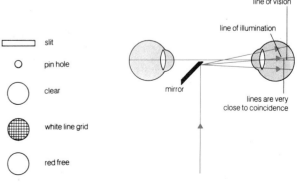

line of vision

line of illumination

mirror

lines are very close to coincidence

OPTICS

Optics, the branch of physics that deals with the nature and behaviour of LIGHT, may be conveniently divided into three main categories. These are termed *geometrical optics*, which deals primarily with the behaviour of rays of light, *physical optics,* which is concerned with the nature of light and its consequent properties and deals with light in terms of waves, and *quantum optics,* which deals with the interaction of light with the atomic entities of matter.

Geometrical optics
Geometrical optics is a method of considering the behaviour of light by assuming that light travels in straight lines through a homogeneous transparent material or *medium* and changes direction only at the boundary between such media. The formation of sharp edged shadows by solid objects placed in the path of a beam of light shows that light can travel in straight lines. The velocity at which it travels through any material is a constant for that material and the maximum value is for light travelling through a vacuum—that is, 186,282.4 mile/s or 299,792.5 km/s. In air, the velocity is very close to its maximum value while on other transparent media, such as glass or water, light travels at significantly lower speeds.

The laws of *reflection* and *refraction* of light are the rules on which the study of geometric optics is based and provide all the information required for predicting and locating the images formed by optical systems involving plane (flat) and curved MIRRORS and LENSES. When a ray of light strikes the interface between two different transparent media, such as glass and air, it generally separates into two weaker rays. One is *reflected* back into the first medium while the other is *refracted :* that is, it enters the second medium but suffers a change in its velocity and consequently changes its direction (bends) whenever it enters at an angle.

The direction of travel of a ray is specified by the angle it makes with the perpendicular, or *normal,* at the point where the ray strikes the interface, the *point of incidence.* The incoming ray and this normal together define a plane, the *plane of incidence.* On reflection, the reflected ray lies in the plane of incidence and the angle of reflection is equal to the angle of incidence. For refraction, the refracted ray lies in the plane of incidence and its direction of travel is determined by the *refractive index* of the materials under consideration. The index of refraction for any material is the ratio of the velocity of light in the material to the velocity of light in vacuum, or for most practical purposes, in air. It was discovered by the Dutch scientist W Snell in 1621 that this index could be determined as the ratio of the SINE of the angle of incidence to the sine of the angle of refraction.

When light travels from a dense into a less dense medium, for example from glass to air, for angles of incidence greater than a certain limiting value, the *critical angle,* the refracted ray disappears and all the light is reflected. This is termed *total internal reflection* and is of considerable importance as the principle governing the use of prisms in optical instruments such as BINOCULARS and the behaviour of glass fibres in FIBRE OPTIC devices.

Physical optics
This is the study of the nature of light. Many optical effects cannot be explained by a simple geometrical approach and such phenomena as DIFFRACTION, *interference* (see INTERFEROMETER) and POLARIZATION can only be understood by considering that light is radiated as a series of WAVES.

If a beam of light passes through a wide slit, and falls on to

Top : the landscape which does not exist. Inhabitants of the Puszta in Hungary can see this remarkable sight daily—the 'Fata Morgana' makes the air seem like a lake of water and the village and trees which seem so near are, in reality, many miles away. The effect is caused by the changing refractive index of air with temperature— turning the air into a gaseous lens.

Above : the apparent 'bending' of a straight stick in water.

a screen, a sharp edged path of light is obtained (as shown by geometrical optics). As the slit is narrowed, however, the situation changes with light spreading into the shadow region. This 'bending' of light, known as *diffraction,* becomes more pronounced as the slit width decreases and is a maximum when the width is of the same order of size as the wavelength of the light used (wavelength is the distance between two successive crests or troughs of the wave). This effect can be explained by considering that any point on a wave front can itself act as a *source* of waves. Thus the slit behaves as a secondary source from which light is transmitted or 'radiated' in all directions.

Two light waves that coincide at a point can interfere with each other. If the crests of one wave coincide with the crests of the other, they are said to be in phase and they reinforce each other. If the crests of one coincide with the troughs of the other, they are out of phase and tend to cancel each other. These conditions define *constructive* and *destructive* interference respectively and between these extremes the waves partially reinforce or cancel each other depending on their phase relationship. An essential condition for interference is that the sources must be *coherent,* that is, they must have the same

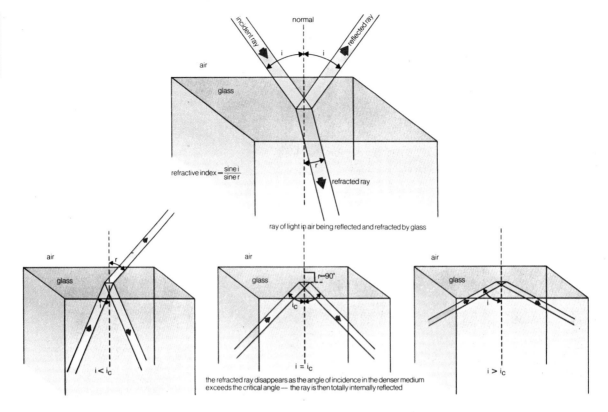

refractive index = $\dfrac{\text{sine } i}{\text{sine } r}$

ray of light in air being reflected and refracted by glass

the refracted ray disappears as the angle of incidence in the denser medium exceeds the critical angle — the ray is then totally internally reflected

frequency and exhibit the same changes of phase. In practice this condition is most easily realized when an incident light wave interacts with its reflection.

This is the process responsible for the colours observable in soap bubbles and thin oil films. Interference patterns produced under controlled conditions can be used as an accurate means of measuring the wavelength of light. An example of this is the *Newton's rings* interference pattern in which a path difference is produced by passing light across a wedge-shaped air gap.

The polarization of light is a consequence of the nature of light waves, which are *transverse*. This means that the vibrations may be in any direction perpendicular to their direction of motion.

If these transverse vibrations are restricted so as to occur in a single plane, the light is said to be *plane polarized*. Synthetically produced polarizing sheet (Polaroid) is a material that renders light plane polarized. It consists of a parallel arrangement of crystals which resolves the direction of the incident vibrations into two directions mutually at right angles and then absorbs one of these components and transmits the other. If two similar sheets of material are placed with their crystal row directions at right angles to each other, light is totally obscured.

In many crystals, such as quartz and calcite, the two perpendicular components of the light vibration are transmitted at different velocities and thus travel in different directions through the crystal. These directions are therefore specified by two different refractive indices. The numerical difference between these indices is called the *birefringence* of the crystal and such behaviour is termed *double refraction*.

Quantum optics   The wave theory of light is unable to provide an explanation of interactions of light and matter on an atomic scale and associated phenomena remained inexplicable until Max PLANCK, in 1900, postulated that a light wave consists of small, highly localized packets or bundles of energy called light *quanta* or *photons* (see QUANTUM THEORY). Subsequent work by Einstein, Bohr and others confirmed the existence of photons and the experimental evidence in support of the theoretical concept soon became conclusive.

The Compton Effect and the photoelectric effect are two phenomena which require the concept of photons for complete explanation. When radiation is incident upon an atom its direction is changed and its frequency decreased. This is the Compton Effect, and is explained by considering an elastic collision between particles, namely an incident photon and an electron in the atom, analogous to the collision between two billiard balls. The photoelectric effect, in which light striking a metal surface causes electrons to be released, results from photons in the incident beam providing energy to the bombarded electrons enabling escape from the metal.

Emission of light energy by the processes of *fluorescence* and *phosphorescence* rely on the increase of the energy of electrons within the atom—atomic excitation. The electrons associated with an atom occupy a limited number of discrete energy levels and can only move to higher energy levels by the provision of discrete bundles of energy provided by photons of the incident light beam.

The relatively modern development of quantum optics has resulted in a much fuller understanding of optical phenomena and has already led to the development of new technologies such as those associated with the LASER.

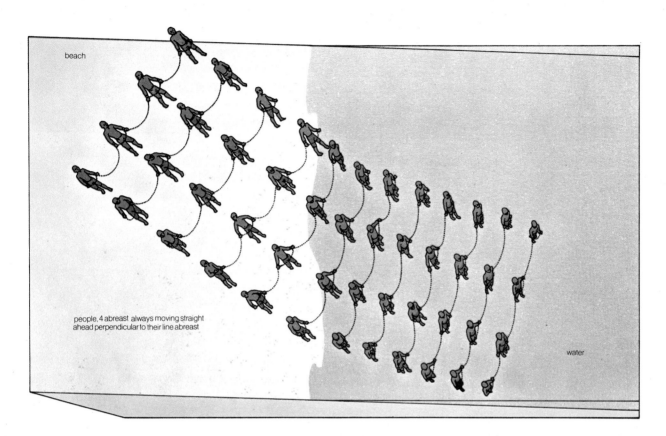

beach

people, 4 abreast always moving straight
ahead perpendicular to their line abreast

water

*Above left: refraction in glass. Incident
light splits into a refracted ray, which is
slightly deviated, and a weaker reflected ray.
When the light passes from glass into air,
the angle of incidence can be such that all the
light reflects. Above: convicts, chained in
lines marching into water at an angle, are
analogous to refraction: their path changes
direction unless they enter at right angles.*

*Near right: the refractive indices of air
and water are different, so the uniform grid
below the globule of water is distorted.
Far right: Newton's rings. These are
caused by interference between reflected and
refracted waves of light. Oil on water
produces such an effect because the oil is of
differing thickness and (depending on this
thickness) will cause either constructive or
destructive interference at each wavelength.*

*Near right: double refraction produced
in Iceland spar crystal. Double refraction is
a property possessed by some materials
having differing refractive indices in different
directions. The result is the formation of
two images.
Far right: caustic curve produced by the
reflection from a spherical surface, which has
diffused focus unlike a parabola.*

MITCHELL BEAZLEY

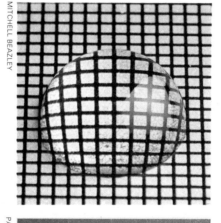

M M RATHORE

PAUL BRIERLEY

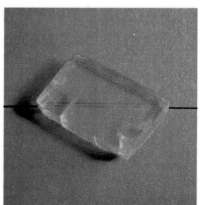

PAUL BRIERLEY

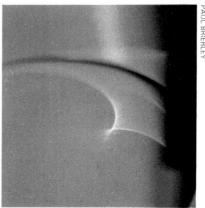

OPTICS PRODUCTION

Methods of producing optical components, such as lenses, mirrors and prisms, have hardly changed in principle since the seventeenth century. The main requirements are that the optical surface should be polished to a highly accurate shape, or *figure*—part of a sphere for lenses and some mirrors, flat for plane mirrors and prisms. The accuracy required is extremely high by normal standards, since the surfaces have to be smoother than the size of waves they are to reflect or refract.

These measurements are so small that they are generally referred to in terms of the wavelength of light, usually the yellow sodium or green mercury spectral lines from DISCHARGE TUBES, with wavelengths of about 5000 angstroms, or 0.5 micron. Thus a surface with a half-wave error would be true to one hundred thousandth of an inch (0.25 micron). In the mirrors of ASTRONOMICAL TELESCOPES, the main mirror may conform to its theoretical curve (a non-spherical figure called a paraboloid) to within a millionth of an inch (0.025 micron). Because reflection bends light through twice the angle of incidence, mirrors need finer surfaces than lenses.

The principle which has always been used to produce both curved and flat surfaces is that if two discs of material are rubbed together with abrasive between them, their irregularities will eventually be smoothed out. If the rubbing motion is back and forth, it might be thought that the result would be a flat surface on both discs. In fact, both become curved, the lower stationary one becoming convex (bulging upwards) and the upper moving one becoming concave (with a hollowed out centre). To ensure a completely symmetrical surface, the lower disc is usually rotated while the upper one is both moved across it and rotated in the opposite direction. A machine can perform both these operations automatically.

The curve which results from this will be very nearly spherical in form. Most optical work relies on this principle even if the components are to be made deliberately non-spherical (*aspheric*) later on. A flat surface is regarded for optical purposes as being part of a sphere with an infinitely large radius: in practice, the surface against which the item is to be ground is made larger than the item itself. Spherical mirror and lens surfaces are defined by their radius of curvature—the radius of the sphere they are part of. This determines how strongly diverging or converging the component is—usually steeper curves are more difficult to make.

Cutting the glass

The raw glass is sawn to outline with a smooth circular saw (or bandsaw) impregnated with diamonds, cooled by a water-soluble oil, which cuts glass very quickly. Although a delicate material, glass can be machined almost like metal using diamond tools. It can be turned in a lathe, have holes drilled in it or rough figuring generated on it with a milling machine. Before such machines were available, optical workers had to grind the glass by hand, using coarse abrasives.

Components thus machined need only one or two successively finer ABRASIVES (usually aluminium oxide powder or garnet with water) to produce a surface smooth enough for polishing. This smoothing operation can be done by machine with a number of components stuck (blocked) with wax or pitch to a jig of the right curve. This block is then worked on an iron tool which has been previously trued up on a *keeper* of opposite form (that is a convex tool has a concave keeper and vice versa). The resulting spherical curve can be checked by optical means or by a *spherometer*—an instrument which mechanically measures the depth of the curve across the lens.

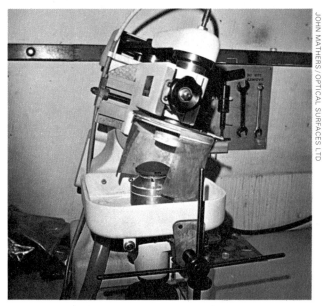

Polishing Precision polishing is usually done on a pre-formed polisher made of pitch (refined from wood or coal) using cerium oxide as a polishing agent. Low quality components may be polished on felt pads instead of pitch, while some optics require special polishing agents. Pitch is a very viscous liquid which conforms slowly to any components worked on it. Some of the skill of optical work is concerned with choosing the correct hardness of pitch because the flowing action of the polisher, changing shape as the work progresses, is critical to producing a good shape.

Other problems are flexure of the glass and the heat produced by FRICTION during work. The glass cools more readily at the edge than the centre and this introduces an important variable in high quality work. This has been partly alleviated by the development of types of glass and CERAMICS having a zero coefficient of expansion over a wide range of temperatures. This is only suitable for reflecting components, rather than lenses, owing to its crystalline structure.

Above left: a modern diamond miller designed for lenses up to 5 inch (13 cm) diameter. The cutting head can be canted over to alter the radius generated; the lens shown on the turntable was generated in a few minutes. The machine stops when the process is finished.

Above: this type of lens polishing machine is widely used to produce medium quality lenses in quantity. A steep block of lenses is shown with the polisher alongside. If Newton's rings indicate that the block has become too steep, this can be corrected by running the machine with the block on top and the polisher underneath. When both sides are polished, the lens edges are milled separately, in such a way that both sides are completely symmetrical.

Below left: final corrections being applied to a prism's angle by hand. The finely grooved pitch tool is kept flat by regular rubbing against the flat 'keeper' seen in the foreground.

Below: a 'tree' of plastic lenses being removed from their mould.

After testing, the components are unblocked and the reverse sides smoothed and polished if required. PRISMS, which have flat faces, are held in metal jigs or plaster blocks in a similar way. Prism angles are checked optically in an *angle dekkor* which compares the job with a master prism of known angle. Correction of the angle is often made by hand (by putting more pressure on one end or the other) and accuracies of half a second of arc can be achieved.

Larger optics (say, above 4 inch—10 cm—diameter), highly curved or best quality components have to be worked singly, which makes them relatively expensive. Aspherics of any quality are made partly by machine but finished by hand. Many such curves can now be moulded, if large quantities are involved, or even turned with a single point diamond (the point of which may be only a molecule in diameter) on a specially developed lathe. Results have been claimed to one-half wavelength but this is not yet a commercial reality.

Testing There are a number of ways in which the various types of optical components can be tested. The most common is to place the surface under test against a reference surface of the shape and accuracy required. As long as the two are approximately the same, *Newton's rings* will be seen—light and dark fringes caused by *interference* (see INTERFEROMETER). These are produced in a similar way to the coloured rings seen on a wet oily road, and are due to the thin wedge of air between the two surfaces. If the two surfaces are exactly the same, no fringes will be seen. To aid visibility, it is usual to examine the fringes of light of one colour only, produced by a sodium or mercury lamp.

For non-standard surfaces, and for producing the reference surfaces, other optical tests are used, the simplest being the *Foucault test*. This uses a knife edge to cut off rays coming from the component which do not go exactly to the focus required, and has the same layout as used for SCHLIEREN TECHNIQUES.

A more recent test involves the interferometry of light when comparing an image with a copy of the object, a ground glass 'scatter plate', that produced the image. This has the advantage of showing up the size of errors in the image, rather than on the optical surface.

These methods only test the image on the optical axis but multiple systems such as camera and projection lenses can now be tested for their *modulation transfer function* or MTF. The image of a test chart, consisting of black and white bars of different spacings, is scanned photoelectrically. The difference between the object and the image can therefore be computed for all points in the field of view of the lens.

Other methods A large proportion of the popular, low priced cameras available today have single plastic moulded lenses. The first plastic lenses were made in 1934 in Britain, and their use is now widespread. They are equivalent in quality to many mass produced glass lenses, though at rather less cost. The plastic—either acrylic or styrene—deforms slightly on setting, but this can be allowed for when making the mould.

A recently developed method for the final working of glass surfaces uses a beam of ions, produced in the same sort of way as in ION PROPULSION devices. Ions of a heavy gas such as argon are used at a potential of about 10 kV, with a beam as narrow as 1 mm. The beam wears down the surface at a rate of about 1 micron an hour—worthwhile only in cases where a fine finish is needed. But for most jobs the accuracies involved can only be achieved by hand and optics will remain a field in which the skilled craftsman is vital.

OPTOELECTRONICS

Optoelectronics is the general term used whenever electronic devices are used in the detection, measurement, transfer or display of visible or INFRA-RED RADIATION. Television is an example of both detection and display. Light from the scene to be televised is detected by a *photoconductive layer,* which decreases its electrical resistance when illuminated, in the TELEVISION CAMERA tube. The camera tube output is converted to a radio frequency signal, transmitted to the receiving aerial and displayed on the CATHODE RAY TUBE in the TELEVISION RECEIVER.

Vacuum tubes such as the cathode ray tube and the PHOTO-MULTIPLIER, which detects very weak light signals and converts them into an easily measurable electric current, are widely used for display and detection. *Semiconductor diodes,* which are used as rectifying devices in ELECTRONICS, however, are increasingly used in optoelectronics as emitters and detectors of radiation.

Semiconductor diodes
A semiconductor DIODE consists of an n-type (electron rich) and p-type (electron deficient) SEMICONDUCTOR separated by a junction or barrier to current flow. A voltage applied in the forward direction reduces the barrier height and the current increases rapidly. Voltage applied in the reverse direction increases the barrier height and virtually no current flows. The diode is used as a radiation detector or *photodiode* with zero or reverse applied voltage. Radiation raises electrons to higher energies, allowing them to cross the barrier, and increases the current or voltage in an external circuit.

If the applied voltage is sufficiently high the photoexcited electrons eject other electrons from atoms with which they collide, giving a much higher *photocurrent.* This is called *ionization by collision* or *avalanche breakdown.* Avalanche diodes are used when the signal carries a wide range of electrical frequencies, as in FIBRE OPTIC communication systems. Transistors are also used as photodetectors.

If the diode is operated in the forward direction the applied voltage will inject electrons across the barrier. These electrons then fall to lower energy levels and emit radiation. The wavelength or colour of the radiation depends on the initial and final electron energies. By introducing impurities into the semiconductor, the energy levels and therefore the colour of the light can be controlled. These devices are called *light emitting diodes* (LEDS).

Display
Light emitting diodes are used to display numeric information in the pocket calculator. By using seven segments, each illuminated by a light emitting diode, in a figure eight configuration any of the numbers 0 to 9 can be formed by illuminating the appropriate segments. More complicated displays, including the letters of the alphabet, can be formed by using larger numbers of diodes. The red emitting diodes in pocket calculators are made from the semiconductor *gallium arsenide phosphide.* Diodes emitting green light are made from *gallium phosphide* with a small amount of nitrogen impurity to provide the required energy level.

Displays can also be made by using DISCHARGE TUBES and LIQUID CRYSTALS. The discharge tube is an evacuated envelope

Below: this thermal vision system displays temperature variations in an object. Infra-red radiation from the scene is focused (using the spherical mirror) on to a plane mirror which oscillates at 16 Hz (the frame rate). Line scan is achieved with the rotating four-sided prism. The radiation is converted into an electrical signal by an indium antimonide crystal and displayed as a 100 line 16 fps picture.

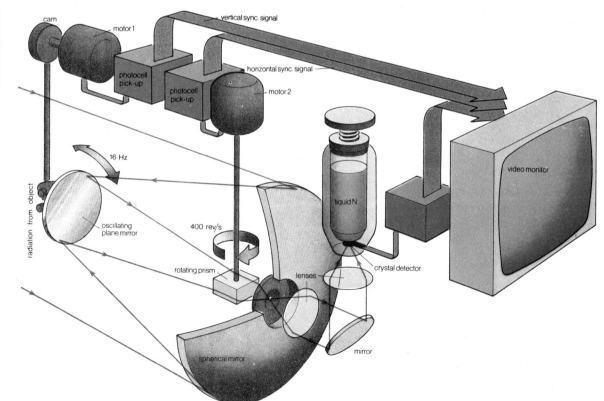

containing a positive and a negative electrode and a small amount of an INERT GAS such as neon. A luminous discharge or *plasma* is excited in the gas when a voltage is applied across the electrodes. Gas discharge displays up to eight inches (20 cm) square are made using a large number of light emitting elements. These are called plasma panels and can be used to display graphical information. In a liquid crystal display the transmission of light through a solution is changed by applying an electric field across the liquid. Liquid crystal displays are used as number indicators in electronic clocks.

Imaging In normal television cameras incident light changes the conductivity of a photoconductive layer by an amount dependent on the light intensity. The photoconductive layer is scanned by an electron beam which converts the conductivity change into an electric signal. For operation at low light levels the photoconductive layer is replaced by an *array* of silicon photodiodes which are sensitive to both infra-red and visible illumination. Camera tubes of this type are employed in security applications and were used in the later Apollo missions to send back colour pictures of the Moon's surface. They may also be used in conjunction with TELE-PHONES, allowing subscribers to see and hear each other and to view documents. These systems are called *videophones*.

There are important advantages in scanning the diode array with an electronic circuit instead of an electron beam. The camera can be made smaller and lighter, it may consume less electrical power and will be more reliable in extreme operating conditions such as space flight. Electronic scanning is achieved using the *metal-oxide semiconductor* (MOS) device developed for electronic circuits. A large two-dimensional array of these devices converts light into electronic charge which is stored under each metal contact. By applying the correct sequence of voltages to each contact, the pockets of charge are transferred from device to device until they reach the output circuit. Here the charge is converted into an electrical signal of the required form. Compact television cameras using such *charge coupled devices* are now commercially available, and cameras capable of transmitting colour pictures have been operated in laboratories.

Imaging devices designed for visible or near infra-red wavelengths detect radiation reflected from the scene being used and cannot work in total darkness. Objects near room temperature, however, emit infra-red radiation with a wavelength of about 10,000 nm (see ELECTROMAGNETIC RADIATION). This radiation can be detected and used to form an image by using semiconductor materials such as *indium antimonide* and *lead-tin telluride* cooled to liquid air temperature. This technique is called *thermal imaging* because the characteristics of the radiation are determined mainly by the temperature of the scene.

Thermal imaging is used in industry and medicine (see ELECTRONICS IN MEDICINE) and in airborne surveillance for both military and peaceful uses. In medical diagnosis it aids the location of conditions which gives rise to localized changes of skin temperature; for example cancerous growths and circulation disorders. Industrial applications include checking furnaces in steel works and glass factories for faults, which show up as hot spots, without stopping production.

Below : this photograph shows a seven segment green emitting gallium phosphide numerical display. Each segment is a light emitting diode (LED) and from these, the characters 0 to 9 can be formed.

Below right : the industry's first monolithic and planar numeric display. This is a gallium arsenide phosphide LED display.

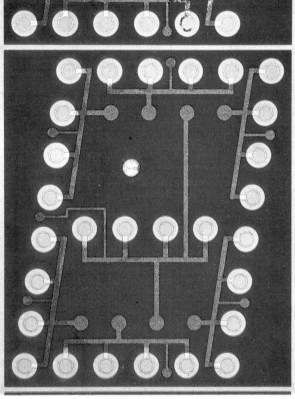

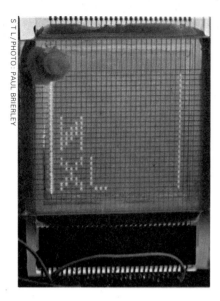

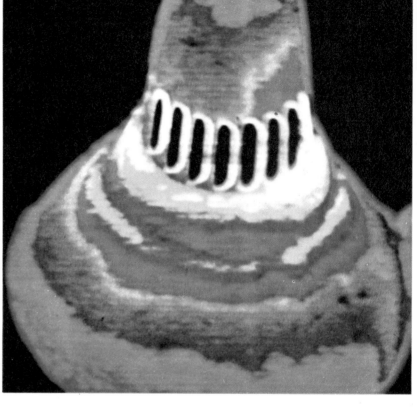

Above : a plasma dot display panel.

Right : colour thermogram of an electric light shade. Each colour represents a different temperature—white is hottest, blue is coldest. It is achieved using a TV-type camera that detects infra-red radiation with up to eight colour filters used sequentially to transfer this from black and white to a colour film.

In both aircraft and satellites thermal imaging systems are used for agricultural, geological and meteorological surveying. For example, since leaf temperature is affected by disease and moisture level, crops needing selective spraying or irrigation can be identified. Finally, the technique has important military applications because it is difficult to camouflage buildings and vehicles emitting heat. Reconnaissance flights can be carried out at night without using artificial illumination.

Measurement Arrays of semiconductor photodetectors have been developed to read numbers and letters. This is called *optical character recognition* and is used for transferring numerical information into computers. In some American post offices it is used to sort mail, since it is faster and more accurate than manual sorting. Until recently most systems scanned the characters with a light spot and measured the intensity of the reflected light with a photomultiplier. By using a two dimensional array of photodiodes whole characters and even pages can be scanned at once, greatly increasing the speed at which information can be transferred.

Silicon photodiodes, because of their more reliable performance, are replacing photomultipliers in many industrial light measuring instruments. In PHOTOMETRY, specially designed FILTERS give the detector a response similar to that of the human eye. Photometers are used to ensure satisfactory standards of lighting in public places, factories and operating theatres. They are also used for standardizing the performance of colour television cameras and receivers, and for many scientific measurements.

Semiconductor diodes and photomultipliers are used in SPECTROSCOPY and star tracking. In emission spectroscopy an electric discharge between two electrodes vaporizes the sample to be analyzed. The wavelength and intensity of the light emitted by the discharge is determined by the elements which are vaporized and the relative quantities in which they are present. The attitude of rockets and satellites is determined by using a silicon diode or photomultiplier to track known stars.

These detectors are also used with light emitting diodes and LASERS, which produce a very intense narrow beam of light, in range finding. Range finders are being developed for military use and, under the name *tellurometers*, for civilian applications. One method of determining range measures the time difference between an outgoing light pulse and the arrival of the reflected pulse from the target, which might be an enemy tank or a nearby hill. Tellurometers are used in the mining and construction industries and in SURVEYING.

Communication In addition to range finding, semiconducting diode lasers are used in fibre optic communication systems. In addition to their high information carrying capacity, these systems have the advantages of freedom from electrical interference and spark hazards. This makes them particularly suitable for data and communication links on aircraft and ships. Over longer distances they are likely to be used for local telephone and television transmission. If optical fibres, however, are used for long distance communication systems the loss in the fibre would be overcome by using repeater stations. These would use a silicon avalanche photodiode and a semiconductor laser or light emitting diode to detect and retransmit the signal. This technique, called *optical coupling,* is already being used in computer systems. Optical coupling demonstrates clearly how electronic devices combined with optics are replacing wholly electronic systems in acquisition, processing and transmission of information.

Left: during the Apollo missions, the craft were able to orbit as low as 10 miles (16 km) from the surface, because the Moon has no air to cause drag.

Above: many comets, such as Comet Mrkos in 1957, have two tails. The straight one is gas, but the curved one is due to dust released from the comet's head, each speck going into its own orbit around the Sun.

ORBIT

The path of a body under the gravitational influence of another is known as an *orbit*. It is the balance between the INERTIA of the moving body and the strength of the gravitational field, and can be illustrated by a bullet being fired horizontally: a bullet from a normal gun will eventually fall to the ground, but if it could be given a high enough initial velocity, the downward curvature of its path would become equal to the downward curvature of the Earth's surface. It would stay at the same height, although falling continuously.

Strictly speaking, the gravitation of the bullet must affect the Earth as well, and the orbit of the bullet is not about the centre of the Earth, but about the centre of gravity of the two bodies (the *barycentre*). Although this correction is negligible for something as light as a bullet it is important when considering the orbit of the Moon, whose mass is 1/81 of the Earth's. Both the Earth and the Moon orbit about their barycentre, which is 3000 miles (5000 km) from the centre of the Earth, only 1000 miles (1600 km) below its surface.

Shapes of orbits

Sir Isaac NEWTON showed in 1687 that as a consequence of his inverse square law of gravitation all orbits must be one of a group of curves known as the *conic sections* (see MATHEMATICS), and in fact some 80 years earlier Johannes KEPLER had found that the planets move in the elongated circles called ellipses (which are conic sections), the Sun being at one of the two focuses. Kepler also discovered that a planet moves fastest when at its closest to the Sun (*perihelion*) and slowest when furthest away (*aphelion*). The average speed of the planets decreases with increasing distance from the Sun: Mercury, the innermost planet, moves at 108,000 mile/hour (47.9 km/sec), the Earth at 67,000 mile/hour

(29.8 km/sec) and the outermost planet, Pluto, at only 10,800 mile/hour (4.8 km/sec).

The other conic sections are the circle, the parabola and the hyperbola. Circular and elliptical orbits are called closed because the orbiting body returns to its starting place; parabolic and hyperbolic orbits extend to infinity and are open, that is, the orbiting body never returns. Some comets' orbits may be hyperbolic, but it is very difficult to distinguish between hyperbolic, parabolic and extremely elongated elliptical orbits from the few observations available when the comets are close to the Earth.

Spacecraft

The principles governing the motion of the planets about the Sun also apply to the orbits of artificial satellites around the Earth. The lowest orbits possible are about 125 miles (200 km) above the Earth's surface, because at lower altitudes the drag of the atmosphere slows down the satellite, and it spirals downwards until it is destroyed by friction with the dense lower atmosphere. At a height of 125 miles the orbital period is about 90 minutes and the speed 18,000 mile/hour (29,000 km/hour). Spacecraft are usually launched eastwards, because then they start with the velocity of the Earth at the latitude of the launch site (about 1600 km/sec at Cape Canaveral) and so they need less expenditure of fuel to reach the orbital velocity. The rotation of the Earth has no other influence on orbital velocities—even if it were to spin ten times faster, the orbital details would be the same.

A particularly important Earth orbit in the present case, however, is that whose height is 22,300 miles (35,700 km), where the period of the orbit is exactly 23 hours 56 minutes, so that a spacecraft appears to remain overhead a particular spot on the Earth's surface. This orbit is used by COMMUNICATION

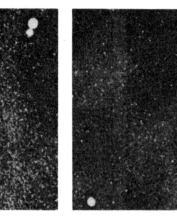

These photographs of the double star Krüger 60 taken in 1908, 1915 and 1920 reveal the motion of the two components about their common barycentre. Such observations are convincing proof that Kepler's and Newton's laws apply even at great distances in the Universe. By measuring the motions of such stars, accurate estimates of their masses can be made. In some cases the smaller star is invisible and is revealed only by the larger one's movements.

SATELLITES (such as Intelsat) so that the ground station can be continuously in contact with them.

A spacecraft travelling at 25,000 miles/hour (40,000 km/hour) will escape from the Earth's gravitational influence and move into an orbit around the Sun. Planetary probes are put into orbits of this kind: for example, a spacecraft to Mars would be put in an elliptical orbit whose perihelion is at the Earth's orbit, and its aphelion at the distance of Mars' orbit. This *Hohmann transfer ellipse* is achieved by accelerating the spacecraft along the direction in which the Earth is moving in its orbit. As a result the probe starts with the orbital velocity of the Earth, and requires only a relatively small increase. The alternative approach, namely to accelerate outwards from the Earth's orbit directly towards Mars, would not use the Earth's velocity as a contribution to the spacecraft velocity, and hence would require a much greater expenditure of fuel. The disadvantage of using the Hohmann ellipse is that the journey takes a long time, 260 days in the case of an Earth to Mars flight, and in practice some extra fuel is used to speed up the flight. The journey of Mariner 9 to Mars in 1971, for example, was reduced to only 192 days.

The most economical method of travelling to the planets between the Earth and Sun, Mercury and Venus, is to use rockets to decrease the spacecraft to a speed less than the Earth's: it will then travel in an ellipse with the distance of Earth as aphelion. In any of these transfer ellipses the target planet must be at the right part of its orbit when the probe arrives there; and hence the launch date of the spacecraft is restricted to a few days each year (the *launch window*) when the Earth and target planet are suitably placed relative to each other.

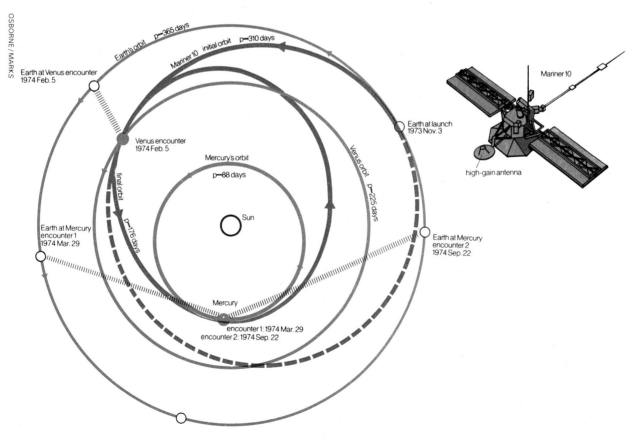

ORBITAL LABORATORY

Man's further progress in space depends on establishing laboratories in Earth orbit in which scientists can experiment under weightless conditions with access to a 'hard' vacuum.

Research already carried out in America's Skylab space station —in which three-man teams spent periods of 28, 59 and 84 days after docking from Apollo spacecraft—suggest that we shall see 'space factories' in which ultrapure metals can be produced in electric furnaces free of contact with containers. In a gravity-free environment it should be possible to manufacture extremely lightweight foamed steel with many of the properties of solid steel; also to combine dissimilar materials like metal and glass and metal and ceramics. Crystals of high purity may be produced for the electronics industry. The weightless environment of the space laboratory should also be ideal for extremely delicate methods of isolating specific biological materials, as in the preparation of concentrated antibodies for the treatment of certain diseases, and in the production of high-purity vaccines.

Orbital laboratories can also be used as stable platforms to examine the surrounding Universe across the entire spectrum of ELECTROMAGNETIC RADIATION reaching the Earth, much of which is cut off from ground observatories by the atmosphere. Detailed examination of the Sun—the nearest star—was made by the Skylab astronauts using the station's Apollo Telescope Mount (ATM).

Inspection of large scale features of the Earth by multi-spectral (false colour) photography has already led to the discovery of unknown mineral deposits, and forests and agricultural areas have been surveyed for general condition, soil quality, moisture content and disease damage. Healthy vegetation shows red or pink on the photos; diseased or impoverished vegetation blue-black.

It has been possible to register thermal patterns in the sea and locate areas of plankton where fish feed. Air and sea pollution have been tracked on a wide scale.

Spacecraft Orbital stations like America's Skylab and Russia's Salyut are launched unmanned by large expendable ROCKETS. They contain systems which allow them to operate for long periods including docking facilities for visiting spacecraft, an airlock, pressurized living quarters, temperature control equipment, GYROSCOPES to keep them stable and gas-jet controls to change their attitude in space. Power to operate onboard systems is obtained from large erectable wing-like solar cell panels which generate electricity from sunlight. Salyut, because it orbits close to the atmosphere, also has a rocket engine for orbital adjustments. It can operate both automatically under remote control and manned.

The further development of orbital laboratories depends on the ability to transport people and material more cheaply between the ground and Earth orbit in SPACE VEHICLES which can be re-used many times. This is the task of America's *space shuttle* being developed for use in the 1980s which will take off vertically like a rocket and land like an aircraft. The winged component, called the *orbiter*, will have a crew of four astronauts. As big as a medium range airliner, it will fly a heavy cargo—up to 65,000 lb (29,484 kg)—into a low orbit, and is capable of being used as an orbiting laboratory in its own right.

Inside the orbiter's 60 ft (18.3 m) long by 15 ft (4.6 m) wide cargo bay will fit the European Spacelab in which four scientists can perform experiments as they orbit the Earth for up to 30 days. This will have two main sections: a pressurized laboratory

Right: Skylab, seen from the Command Module during the final inspection after a mission, was highly successful despite incidents such as the loss of a solar panel which led to overheating. The Mylar parasol, rigged up by the astronauts to reduce the Sun's heating, is visible in this view.

Left: Mariner 10 flew past Venus once and Mercury twice during 1974, taking TV shots. The first orbit was a Hohmann transfer ellipse which would normally have brought the craft back to the vicinity of Earth. But by approaching close to Venus, the craft made use of the planet's orbital energy to alter its own course towards Mercury.

Its new orbit was chosen to have a period of 176 days—twice Mercury's. Thus both Mariner and Mercury return to the same spot in space every 176 days. At each encounter with a planet, TV pictures and other data were transmitted back to Earth.

PHOTRI

solar array

multiple docking adaptor

external avionics & telemetry equipment

auxiliary docking port

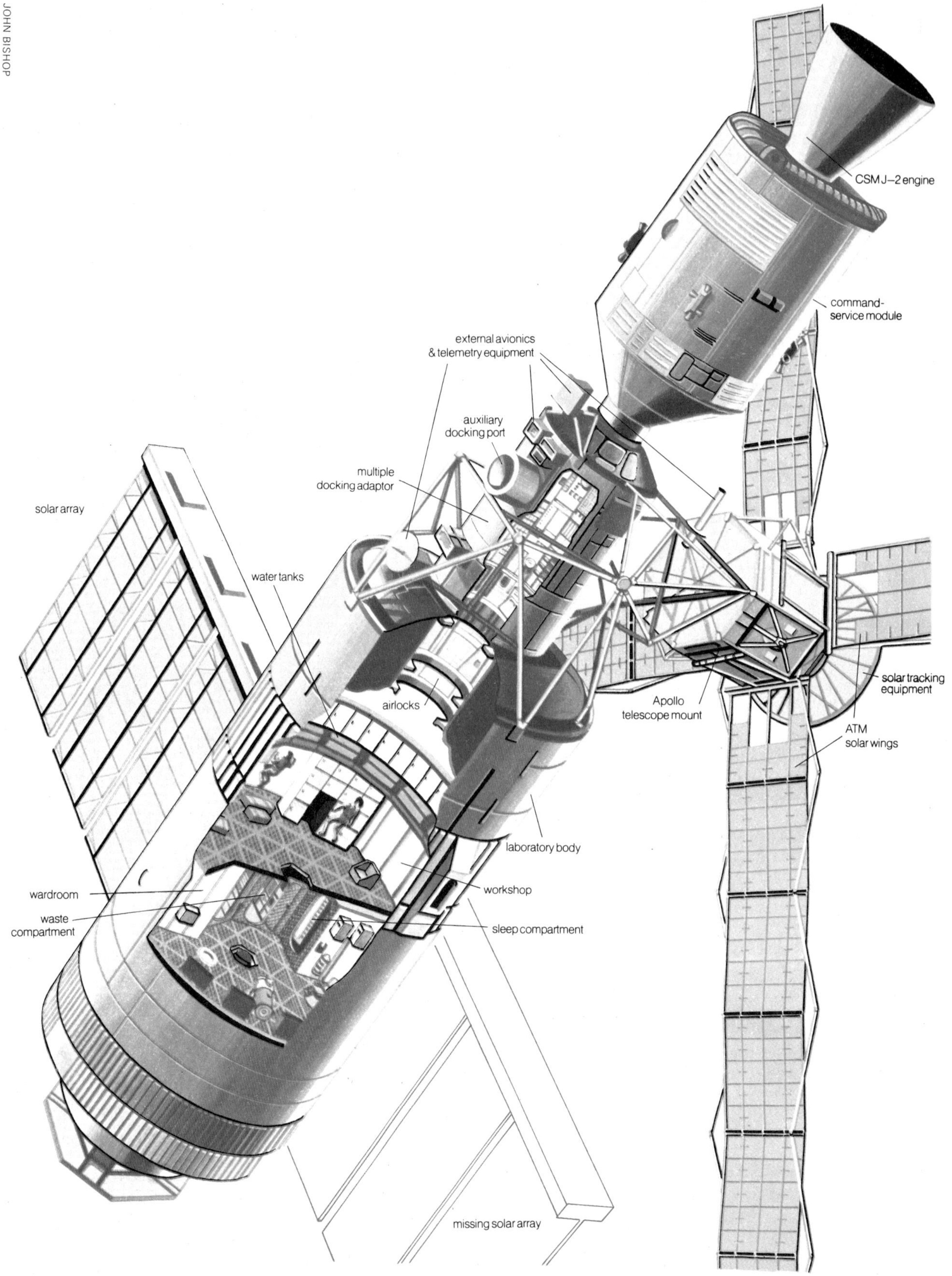

CSM J-2 engine

command-service module

water tanks

airlocks

wardroom

waste compartment

workshop

laboratory body

sleep compartment

Apollo telescope mount

solar tracking equipment

ATM solar wings

missing solar array

module in which the research team will work in a 'shirtsleeve environment' (that is, without the need for spacesuits), and an external platform, or pallet, for mounting large man-directed instruments such as telescopes or antennae requiring direct exposure to space. The Lab itself will have standard laboratory instruments, equipment racks, work benches, data recording and processing equipment, and extendable booms for remote positioning of certain experiments in the space environment.

According to the National Aeronautics and Space Administration, the US space agency, the researchers who fly in Spacelab will be healthy men and women, qualified in their field, and requiring only a few weeks of specialized training.

At the end of the mission Spacelab will be flown back to base with the research team to land on a conventional runway. On the ground—while the orbiter is being prepared for another flight—the Lab can be lifted out and exchanged for another containing different experiments.

Beyond Spacelab is the opportunity to assemble large space stations in orbit from prefabricated modules. The modules would be ferried up piece by piece by the shuttle and docked together.

Left: the whole Skylab configuration, complete with command and service module, is shown in this cutaway view. The conical command module is the only part to return to Earth. The laboratory was built inside the third stage of a Saturn V rocket, measuring some 48 × 22 feet (14.6 × 6.7 m), originally destined for a Moon mission which was then cancelled. The Apollo telescope mount was in line with the third stage during launch, with its solar panels folded up. It then swung out and the solar panels deployed, making room for the combined command and service modules to dock with the workshop.

ORGAN, electronic

The essential and obvious difference between the pipe organ (see ORGAN, pipe) and its electronic namesake is that, in the electronic organ, the vibrations of the air and eventual amplification of the sound wave are brought about by electronic rather than mechanical means. Generally speaking, this difference in the origin of the sound waves should not distinguish the sounds reaching the ear because, having produced the required contour in an electrical signal, it is only necessary to convert the waves of the current into air-pressure waves of the same form and character, to radiate the same sound to the ear as would occur in a natural or mechanical process. The accuracy with which electronic sound can be created to resemble natural or mechanical tones is related to the form of the wave shape generated and its subsequent modification by the tone-forming filters (see FILTER, electrical) in order to re-create the *harmonics* or *overtones* of the model sound.

Electronic methods The two most widely used methods of wave generation in electronic organs are *electromagnetic* and *electrostatic*. An electromagnetic generator produces oscillations by the movement of a conductor in a magnetic field, or the reverse; electrostatic generators rely on the alteration of the capacitance of a CAPACITOR in the VALVE circuit which originates the currents to generate the partial tones. The Hammond organ employs a series of rotating magnetic generators driven by a synchronous motor and coupled to a gearing system set to reproduce a semitone pitch change. Each rotating wheel is polygonal in shape, and as each high point of the disc passes before the magnet, an electric current is induced in the coil which surrounds the magnet. The resultant alternating current produces the component tones on to which can be

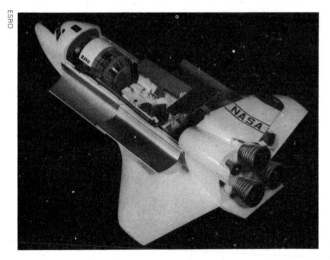

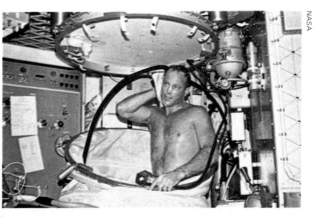

Above: a model of the projected Spacelab in the space shuttle's cargo bay. The Lab is being built by the European Space Agency (ESRO), and may be used for up to 50 flights on the space shuttle.

Above right: astronaut Owen Garriott during a 59 day Skylab mission, at the telescope controls. The Sun's image was displayed on two screens in the centre of the panel, one with a Polaroid camera for instant photography. Garriott's shoes are locked in a triangular grid, used all over Skylab, to keep him in place. Behind him is the airlock and beyond that is the main working area. At right, drying off after a space shower. The astronaut uses a hand held water spray and a vacuum hose to suck up the droplets, with the curtain up.

superimposed the desired characteristics of *timbre*, *attack*, and *volume*. The Compton organ makes use of belt-driven rotating electrostatic generators which have been engraved with a selection of waveforms. The first commercial instruments generated a square waveform. This square waveform contains only the odd number harmonics and therefore precludes its use for an accurate imitation of sounds such as flute or string tone, which require even number harmonics. Clarinets and bassoons, on the other hand, are served well by the square waveform. Both odd and even number harmonics are contained in a sawtooth wave form, but for the clearest imitation of orchestral colours, the harmonics need to be available independently. A square waveform can be created from a sawtooth waveform, if frequency division is employed, by reversing the input phase and combining with it the sawtooth waveform of the octave below. Both the original sawtooth waveform and the newly created substantially square waveform can then be filtered to form two quite different tone colours. It is also possible to obtain the two waveforms by taking one from the anode circuit of the generator and the other from a transformer in the cathode circuit.

To this generated pitch can now be added the various elements of timbre such as harmonics, overtones and the very important *formant*, the part of the tone which leads to recognition by the ears. The Hammond organ uses voltage variation to add timbre and, in addition, it has a second series of generator wheels 'tuned' flat and sharp to the main generator, producing a very soft beat note to enhance the quality of the sound. The famous Wurlitzer organ (which uses an electrostatic generator consisting of vibrating brass reeds acting as variable capacitors, with a fan supplying the wind pressure) produces a complex waveform from which can be extracted, by suitable deployment of the pick-ups, the harmonics giving the natural tone quality to the reeds, which are then treated electronically so as to accentuate some and reduce or remove others.

After the tone forming circuit of the organ has been passed, other sound qualities can be added. Vibrato is usually obtained by low frequency OSCILLATORS which modulate the main tones at a given rate. Organs such as the Novachord and the Solovox can produce either percussive notes (like the harpsichord) or sustained notes (like the pipe organ) from the same wave form by the use of variable resistors that give a range of 'attack' times. (The pitch is not affected, having the same wave form and harmonics; only the time-frequency is changed.)

Other instruments   Many other types of organs have been built, as well as instruments such as the Electrochord which is basically an amplified piano that can have its attack and

Below, left, and right: Boosey and Hawkes, the music publishers, have an electronics division which makes a group of electronic organs and pianos. Left is the Diamond 800, which has a 13-note C to C pedal board with 16' and 8' 'sustain' tabs; below is a close-up of the voice tabs; below that is the 550, which has automatic chords, bass and rhythm; below right is the 550 wiring.

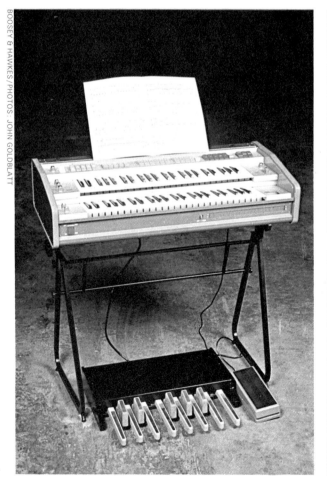

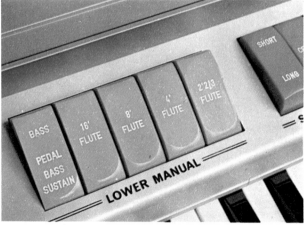

decay characteristics, and the harmonic content of its sound varied electronically. Possibly the best known instrument of musical (but not commercial) interest is the Trautonium. This instrument retains the variable pitch potential of an electronic pitch generator, and is therefore able to play a 'slide' scale or music requiring micro-tone intervals. A keying device can be fitted with a note sign attached opposite the relevant part of the generator in order to pre-select a pitch and it can therefore be played either in a conventional manner or making use of a 'slide' technique. Vibrato on the Trautonium is achieved by moving the tuning contact either side of the mean position, but this requires considerably more skill from the performer than with oscillator systems. In the case of the Organova, sound waves are created by varying the intensity of a beam of light which is directed on to a PHOTOELECTRIC CELL thereby setting free a current of correspondingly fluctuating intensity. Of more commercial value is the Hammond Chord-Organ on which the left hand operates 'chord-buttons' that select the correct three or four notes (and two pedal notes) which will harmonize the note played on the melodic keyboard by 'tuning' the six chord oscillators. Basically then, by depressing a key and pre-setting the *stops* and *couplers*, the player makes a selection of the desired frequencies of all seven overtones in their relative intensities and with added tone colours. It is then a simple matter to pass this 'compound' tone through a pre-amplifier stage (usually located in the console) and then to the major amplification system.

ORGAN, pipe

In theory the pipe organ is a simple instrument; in practice it is complex. It is rightly called the King of Instruments. Not only is it the largest instrument but also the most versatile, in terms of the loudness and variety of sounds it can produce, as well as its range, from low notes which are felt rather than heard to notes so high that they can be painful to hear.

The organ works on a similar principle to the primitive 'pipes of Pan'. These pipes were bundles of hollow reeds bound together: a tune was produced by blowing across the tops of the reeds, each of a different length and producing a different note. In an organ, a mechanical device provides more wind than can be produced by human lungs, and another mechanism delivers the wind to the selected pipe. Unlike the wind instruments of the orchestra, where one pipe is adapted to play many notes, the organ has a separate pipe for each note.

Early organs Crude organs existed in Roman times. Early organs were used in churches to accompany choral singing; they had only one row of pipes, called a *rank*, with a range of about the same as the human voice, a range smaller than that of the modern PIANO. (The keyboard of an organ is

Below: a drawing of an organ with bellows worked by levers, from a manuscript of the twelfth century, in the library of Trinity College, Cambridge. The people who worked the bellows were usually apprentices, and it was tedious work. Nowadays the wind is kept up by means of electric fans.

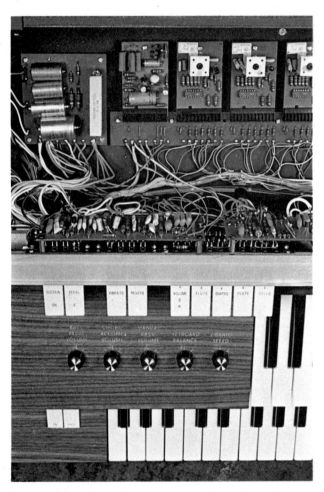

still smaller than that of the piano: 61 notes as against 88). This range is known as *unison pitch*: the rank which sounds it is called the *eight foot* rank, after the length of the open pipe, usually the largest in the rank, which sounds two octaves below Middle C, with a frequency of 64 hertz (cycles per second).

An open pipe of four feet, half the length, will sound an octave higher, two feet another octave higher, and so forth. Similarly, doubling the length of any open pipe will make it sound an octave lower (see MUSICAL SCALE). Lengths of feet are still used for organ pipes in Continental Europe.

On the early organs, there was not much variety of tone available because the note always sounded the same whether the key was touched lightly or heavily. When extra ranks were added, the appropriate pipes from each rank all sounded together when the key was pressed. This made a loud brilliant noise, so for quieter passages a smaller organ was added, tuned to two feet and played from a separate *manual* (keyboard). Gradually the instruments were combined and the keyboards set one above the other.

At about the same time, to save wind (which was then generated by muscle power) and to give variety and greater control when the organ was used as a solo instrument, a mechanism was devised to allow the player to stop off certain ranks and select the ones to sound. These controls, usually draw-knobs placed on either side of the manuals, are called *stops*. Four main types of pipe have evolved, whether made nowadays of metal or wood, according to their tonal quality: diapason, the original organ sound; flute; gamba, a sound resembling that of a string instrument; and reed, which on some instruments has a fiery brass sound and on others a mellower oboe or bassoon sound. Types of pipes as well as ranks can be selected and combined using stops.

Since the fourteenth century, a pedal board operated by the player's feet has been used to control the longer pipes. During the eighteenth century another pedal was incorporated to help control the volume of sound by operating shutters on a *swell box* enclosing the pipes of one or more manuals. A *coupler* mechanism is used to combine stops or to connect manuals to pedals.

Modern organs   Each rank has the same number of pipes as there are keys on the manual, usually 61. A medium sized organ with 30 stops on three manuals and pedal will have no fewer than 1656 pipes. (The pipes which can be seen on an organ are only a small proportion of the total.) Organs of this size and larger were common in the Netherlands and North Germany in the seventeenth century and were the subject of great civic pride and competition. (In 1705, J S Bach is said to have walked from Lüneburg to Lübeck, over 200 miles or 322 km, to hear Dietrich Buxtehude play the organ.) These seventeenth century instruments are still used when making recordings of the music of the sixteenth to eighteenth century, and many musicians believe they have never been surpassed for tonal quality. Yet they were built before the Industrial Revolution and rely for their vital air-tightness on the quality of their mainly wooden construction. (The oldest organ still in use having modern characteristics was built about 1380 in the church at Sion, in the canton of Valais in Switzerland.)

The mechanism required to control these instruments must be light, quick acting and trouble free. The pipes are wider than the keys, so mechanical means must be used to spread the vertical motion of the keys to ranks of pipes which can be many feet wide or even on the opposite wall of the church.

Construction   The *console* is the name given to the assembly of keyboards and controls. The *action* between key and pipe is called a *tracker action*; it is a system of bell cranks, rods, wires, valves and rollers. When a key, mounted on a fulcrum, is depressed, the other end rises; a rod transmits this vertical motion to an arm on a roller, which in turn transmits it laterally to a similar arm below the pipe which is to sound. This second arm draws down a wire (*tracker*) which opens a spring-loaded pallet valve; through this valve air passes to the chamber on which all the pipes controlled by that key are mounted. (Which pipes sound depends upon which stops have been selected.) When the key is released the spring closes the valve.

The action of the stop is transmitted, again by rods and cranks, to a thin strip of wood called a *slider*, mounted between the air channel and the base of the pipe. When a drawstop is pulled the slider moves so that a hole in it lines up with the base of the pipe and allows the pipe to sound. Today many organs operate the valves and stops by means of solenoid switches actuated from the console or by compressed air, methods which simplify transmission of motion. Many

Right : the tracker action. The ranks of pipes are wider than the keyboard, so the mechanical action must be transmitted sideways. Depressing a key operates a horizontal roller which transmits the movement through a system of levers and springs to a pallet valve, which allows air from the bellows to enter the pipe. Electric actions have been built, but the mechanical are still preferred.

Below : a fifteenth century painting by Jan van Eyck, showing the early type of organ with a range about that of the human voice.

ALLARD GRAPHIC ARTS

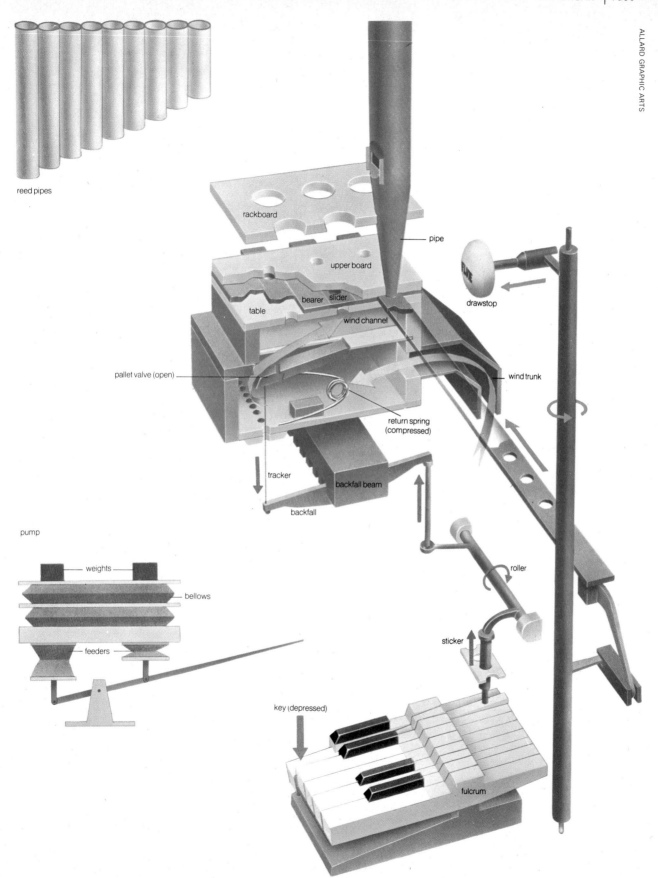

reed pipes

rackboard

pipe

upper board

bearer   slider

table

wind channel

drawstop

pallet valve (open)

return spring
(compressed)

wind trunk

tracker

backfall beam

backfall

pump

weights

bellows

feeders

roller

sticker

key (depressed)

fulcrum

Below: a fancy organ built in the seventeenth century in the chapel of the Residenz, a palace in Munich. It is decorated with miniatures painted on parchment, as well as cameos and pieces of turquoise and coral. The pipes are silver-plated and gilded.

Below right: an organ builder at work. For centuries the construction of organs of superb quality was accomplished by painstaking handwork, especially cabinet work which had to be airtight in order to allow the wind supply to be kept up. Tracker action in some organs was still operational after being neglected for generations. In the nineteenth century designers tried to make the instrument into a substitute for the symphony orchestra, and it fell out of favour with many composers and musicians, but since World War 1 traditional values in organ building have been revived, partly as a result of scholarship in music history.

recitalists still prefer tracker action, and many organs are still built with it, because of the more intimate control it provides.

A plentiful supply of wind (air under mild compression) is essential, and the pressure must not fluctuate. For centuries leather bellows were used to raise the pressure, at first of the simple blacksmith's forge type but developing into a powerful pump with twin bellows alternatively feeding a large pleated leather reservoir. Weights placed on top of the reservoir provided sufficient pressure supply.

The bellows were driven by the muscle power of several men working long levers or treadles. Muscles were supplanted by steam at first; today the wind supply is generated almost universally by electrically driven fan blowers.

ORGAN, REED (see harmonium)

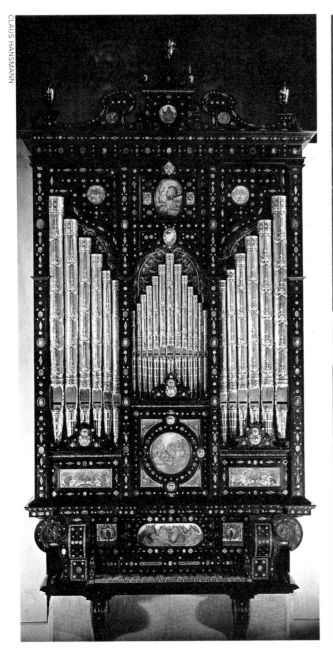

ORGANIC CHEMISTRY

Organic chemistry is the study of chemical COMPOUNDS which contain carbon ATOMS. It is perhaps surprising that an entire branch of chemistry should be devoted to compounds of a single ELEMENT, but more carbon-containing compounds are known than compounds derived from all the other elements put together. INORGANIC CHEMISTRY is concerned with the chemistry of all the elements and those compounds which do not contain carbon atoms (with the exception of the oxides and sulphides of carbon and the metal carbonates, which are considered to be more akin chemically to inorganic rather than organic compounds).

Organic chemistry developed as a field of study in its own right in the middle of the 19th century, and was so called because it dealt with chemical compounds derived from *living* sources—as distinct from other known substances which were derived from *mineral* sources. It was later discovered that almost all these compounds from living matter contained carbon atoms, and the term organic chemistry was extended to include all other carbon-containing compounds. Until the mid 1800s organic compounds were thought to possess a 'life force' which set them apart from inorganic compounds. Not surprisingly, this belief did nothing to encourage the development of organic chemistry on a rational basis, and the concept lingered on even after Wöhler had synthesized the organic compound *urea*, $CO(NH_2)_2$, from the purely inorganic compound *ammonium cyanate*, NH_4CNO, in 1828.

Bonding

In 1858 the German chemist Kekulé and the Scottish chemist Couper published independent papers concerning the arrangement of atoms within organic MOLECULES. They both recognized the importance of VALENCY, that is the power of atoms to combine with each other. Carbon, for example, has a valency of four, nitrogen a valency of three, oxygen a valency of two, and hydrogen a valency of one, and the HALOGENS a valency of one. The HYDROCARBON methane has the molecular formula CH_4 and the four hydrogen atoms are equally spaced around the carbon atom; there are four chemical BONDS to the carbon atom and one to each of the hydrogen atoms, so the valencies of the atoms are satisfied. By far the most common type of bonding between atoms in organic molecules is *covalent* bonding, and it is achieved by the sharing of electrons. A carbon atom normally has four electrons in its outer electron 'shell', although the shell has a capacity of eight electrons. Similarly, chlorine, a halogen, has seven electrons in its outer electron shell which, like carbon, has a capacity of eight electrons.

A full electron shell is more stable than a partly filled one, and in the compound carbon tetrachloride, CCl_4, electrons are shared between the carbon atoms and the four chlorine atoms so that each atom is effectively surrounded by a full outer electron shell. Each bond between the central carbon atom and one of the chlorine atoms is composed of a pair of electrons, one derived from the carbon atom and one derived from the chlorine atom. The following diagrams represent molecules of carbon tetrachloride, chloromethane, CH_3Cl and methanol, CH_3OH. Although all the electrons are identical, they are coloured differently to indicate their source.

carbon tetrachloride   chloromethane   methanol

Isomerism

It is fairly common for different chemical compounds to have the same molecular formula. Thus, the formula C_6H_{12} can represent a number of different hydrocarbons, including *cyclohexane* and *hexene-1* which are distinct from each other and have different chemical and physical properties. Cyclohexane is a saturated compound having six $-CH_2-$ groups linked together in a ring, whereas hexene-1, $CH_2 = CHCH_2CH_2CH_2CH_3$, is an unsaturated straight-chain compound; the two compounds are said to be *structural isomers* of each other.

In 1848 Pasteur was studying the way polarized light (see POLARIZATION) passes through solutions of tartaric acid, and he discovered that there were two distinct forms of the acid which were identical chemically but which rotated the plane of polarized light in different directions. He concluded that the structure of the two forms was the same, but that the various chemical groups were differently arranged in space. A similar situation is observed with lactic acid, $CH_3CH(OH)COOH$, which has two 'optically active' forms. The reason for this is that lactic acid has four *different* chemical groups ($-CH_3$, $-H$, $-OH$ and $-COOH$) attached to the same central carbon atom, and there are two different ways of arranging the groups around the carbon atom. A good way to visualize this is to paint each corner of a pyramid shaped (tetrahedral) milk carton with a different colour (each colour representing one of the four chemical groups), place the container in front of a mirror and paint a second similar container to correspond with the image. It will be found that the two containers are

Below: a photograph taken in 1870 of Friedrich Wöhler, the German chemist, who was the first man to synthesize an organic compound (urea) from an inorganic source.

DAYMARK

painted differently; they cannot be superimposed on each other so that the colours correspond. The two isomers of lactic acid can be represented as follows:

Isomers of this type are called optical isomers or *stereoisomers,* and they are important because the chemical compounds present in living tissue, for example the AMINO ACIDS, are generally of a specific stereoisomeric type.

Organic compounds

Organic compounds can be divided into four main categories: ALIPHATIC COMPOUNDS, AROMATIC COMPOUNDS, *alicyclic compounds* and *heterocyclic compounds.* Aliphatic compounds are open chain compounds and include such compounds as methane, CH_4, acetone, CH_3COCH_3, n-octane, $CH_3(CH_2)_6CH_3$, acetic acid, CH_3COOH, and PLASTICS such as polyethylene. Aromatic compounds are derived from the HYDROCARBON benzene, C_6H_6, and examples include toluene, $C_6H_5CH_3$, aniline, $C_6H_5NH_2$, and trinitro-toluene (TNT), $C_6H_2(CH_3)(NO_2)_3$:

toluene

aniline

trinitrotoluene

Alicyclic compounds are compounds which contain rings of carbon atoms, but not benzene rings. Cyclohexane, an industrial solvent, cyclohexanone, which is used in the manufacture of nylon-6, and cyclopropane, an anaesthetic gas, are all examples of alicyclic compounds:

cyclohexane

cyclohexanone

cyclopropane

Near right: cooling solidified droplets, or prills, of urea in a fluidized bed. Urea is used as a fertilizer and in the manufacture of glues and synthetic resins.

Centre right: an X-ray diffraction photograph of a crystal of a benzene compound. The picture was made using a special lens so that the pattern of spots corresponds to the arrangement of atoms in the molecule. A hexagonal benzene ring can be seen in the centre.

Heterocyclic compounds are ring compounds in which there is at least one atom in the ring which is not a carbon atom. Examples include the amino acids *histidine* and *proline:*

histidine

proline

In order to simplify the writing out of chemical formulae, it is usual practice to omit carbon and hydrogen atoms where they appear in rings. Thus, toluene, cyclohexanone and proline are normally written as follows:

toluene

cyclohexanone

proline

Organic compounds can also be classified according to the chemical groups which they contain. Among the more common groups are ALDEHYDE groups, -CHO, amino groups (see AMINE), $-NH_2$, CARBOXYLIC ACID groups, -COOH, ethyl groups, $-C_2H_5$, hydroxy groups (see ALCOHOL), -OH, keto groups (see KETONE), -CO-, methyl groups, $-CH_3$, and nitro groups, $-NO_2$. Aniline, therefore, is an aromatic amine and cyclohexanone is an alicyclic ketone. The reactions which organic compounds undergo will depend on the various groups they contain; a particular group will normally undergo the same reactions whatever molecule it may be part of, although its behaviour can be, and often is, influenced by the groups attached to it in the molecule. Ketones, for example,

BASF

can be reduced (see OXIDATION AND REDUCTION) to give hydroxy compounds and will react with *hydroxylamine,* NH_2OH, to give *oximes:*

$$CH_3COCH_3 + H_2 \rightarrow CH_3CHOHCH_3$$

acetone   hydrogen   isopropyl alcohol

$$CH_3COCH_3 + NH_2OH \rightarrow CH_3CHOHCH_3 + H_2O$$

acetone   hydroxylamine acetone oxime   water

It is a knowledge of the reactions of the various chemical groups and how they will behave in particular situations that allows the organic chemist to synthesize particular compounds from available raw materials.

Determination of the structure of an unknown chemical compound is done by physical and chemical methods of analysis. The chemical reactions of the compound will give an indication of the chemical groups present, and the compound can often be broken down into smaller, more easily recognizable fragments. Physical methods include molecular weight determination (see MOLECULE), infra-red and ultra-violet SPECTROSCOPY, NUCLEAR MAGNETIC RESONANCE, and MASS SPECTROSCOPY. Many organic compounds are extremely complex, and determination of their structure has taken many years of painstaking research. The following structures have been worked out for strychnine and chlorophyll:

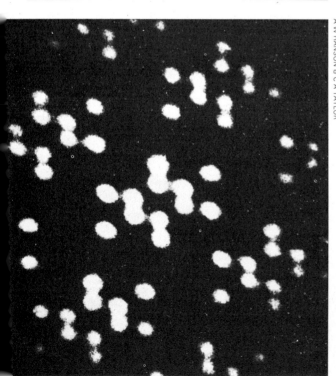

strychnine

chlorophyll

ORTHICON (see television camera)

OSCILLATOR

One of the simplest kinds of oscillator is the PENDULUM, whose motion can be expressed graphically as a SINE wave. A pendulum will continue to swing with the same amplitude (in this case distance of swing) only if ENERGY just sufficient to meet its losses (due, for example, to air friction) is replaced at an appropriate time each swing. In an electronic oscillator, where it is electrons which are made to oscillate, similar replacements of energy loss must be made if oscillations are to be maintained.

In addition to electronic oscillators which generate sinusoidal (sine wave) oscillations like the pendulum, others produce non-sinusoidal oscillations, for example the *square wave* and *sawtooth* pulse generators. The wave form of the oscillations provides a simple means of classifying electronic oscillations.

In all electronic oscillators the ultimate source of energy is a direct current (dc) power supply. AMPLIFIERS, and FEEDBACK, *tuned* and *relaxation* circuits serve to convert dc energy into alternating current (ac) energy.

The time interval between identical successive points on a wave is called the *period* of oscillation, and the number of oscillations (or cycles) completed in a given time (usually one second) is termed the *frequency.* The unit of frequency is the Hertz (Hz), 1 Hz being one cycle per second.

Sinusoidal oscillators When a CAPACITOR is discharged through a low resistance inductor (see INDUCTANCE), the current is oscillatory and has a frequency equal to the resonant frequency of the circuit (see RESONANCE), that is, the frequency at which the circuit offers the least opposition to current flow. Owing to circuit RESISTANCE, however, and consequent loss of energy, the oscillations will fade away and eventually cease unless the energy lost is replaced. A measure

Below: a quartz crystal hybrid structure used in oscillators. Quartz is a piezoelectric material, that is, when it is squeezed, a voltage is created and vice versa. Coupling these properties produces oscillations.

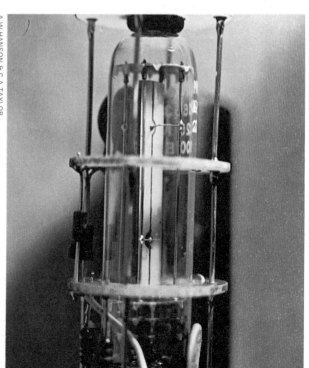

Above: a modern signal generator. The central area is for locating a precise frequency in the range 10 kHz to 88 MHz. Calibration is achieved using the crystal oscillators (bottom right) and the signal can be either amplitude or frequency modulated (at top).

Below right: during oscillations energy changes form. In pendulums and springs, kinetic energy of motion interchanges with potential energy. In electrical oscillators, energy in magnetic field (due to movement of charge) interchanges with stored charge on a capacitor.

of the losses is given by the Q factor of the tuned circuit. One definition of Q is the ratio of stored to dissipated energy. A high Q circuit will oscillate for a great many cycles before 'dying', while a low Q circuit will oscillate for relatively few cycles. A high Q factor also implies precise tuning.

One method of replacing the lost energy in a tuned circuit (sometimes called a *tank circuit*) to maintain the oscillations is to couple the inductor in the tuned circuit with a second inductor (this is called a transformer). The signal obtained by transformer action in this second inductor is fed into an amplifier, and the output from this applied to the tuned circuit. The amplified signal must be at least equal in magnitude to the oscillating signal from which it was derived and be *in phase* with it (signals in phase reach a maximum and minimum together and are at identical positions in their respective cycles at all times). The circuit operates on the principle of *positive feedback*.

This type of oscillator is used to generate frequencies of from a few thousand hertz up to hundreds of kilohertz and even several megahertz. *Crystal controlled* oscillators are employed where a stable frequency is required in the range 400 Hz to 200 MHz. The oscillator depends on the PIEZO-ELECTRIC effect of certain crystals (for example quartz) which generate electrical oscillations when subjected to mechanical strain, or conversely oscillate structurally when a suitable voltage is applied. These oscillations are maintained, and the oscillator thereby controlled at the resonant frequency of the high Q crystal, by supplying the latter with energy from an LC (inductor-capacitor) circuit driven by an amplifier.

Magnetostriction oscillators are based on materials such as nickel which exhibit a small change in their dimensions when subjected to a magnetic field; conversely, if their dimensions are altered by an external force their magnetic properties change (see MAGNETISM). The material is excited at its mechanical resonant frequency, where these effects are most pronounced, by current flowing in a coil wound around the material. A separate coil on the material, or a variable reluctance or capacitive pick-up, provides a feedback signal which, when amplified, is used to maintain oscillation.

Magnetostriction and crystal oscillators are often used where it is desired to transmit the electrical oscillations to another medium, as in ULTRASONIC generators for example.

The phase shift oscillator has no tuned circuit, but uses a ladder network of three resistors and three capacitors to feed the output of a single stage resistively loaded amplifier back to its input. The values of the resistors and capacitors are chosen so that at the desired frequency of oscillation (f_0) there is a half-cycle difference (180° of phase shift) between the input and output voltages of the network. Since there is also a 180° phase difference between the amplifier input and output signal voltages, there is a total of 360° of phase shift at frequency f_0 around the loop formed by the ladder network and the amplifier. As long as the amplification of the signal through the amplifier is greater than its attenuation through the network, oscillations are obtained.

Another type of phase shift oscillator is the Wien Bridge oscillator which employs resistors and capacitors in a bridge circuit. Phase shift oscillators are often used in audio frequency applications.

Non-sinusoidal oscillators Valves [vacuum tubes] and transistors which provide amplification in sinusoidal oscillators act as SWITCHES in many non-sinusoidal oscillators where the frequency of oscillation depends on the time constants of associated circuits. Non-sinusoidal oscillators are *relaxation* type oscillators, so called because a sudden change or relaxation of the circuit conditions generates the waveform.

A simple square-wave oscillator can be made by coupling the output of an amplifier (with 180° phase shift between its input and output signals) to its own input through a capacitor, a second similar amplifier, and a further capacitor. A small signal at the input of the first amplifier trying to switch on the amplifier will be amplified by both amplifiers, fed back to augment the original signal, amplified again, and so on. This produces an 'avalanche' effect which switches on the first amplifier and switches off the feedback amplifier.

After a period determined by the circuit time constants, the varying voltages on the coupling capacitors produce a second avalanche effect, resulting in the first amplifier being switched off and the feedback amplifier being switched on. Following a further period related again to the circuit time constants, the first amplifier will start to switch on and the whole sequence of events will be repeated, giving a series of square waves at the output of the first amplifier. Applications of square wave generators include timing functions in TELE-VISION, COMPUTERS, and RADAR.

Requirements often arise for basically triangular pulses of large amplitude and short duration (fractions of a microsecond up to a millisecond) compared to the period of oscillation. In such applications, instead of a multivibrator (see LOGIC CIRCUITS), a blocking oscillator may be preferred where the gain provided by the transformer provides a large in-phase feedback signal causing rapid switching. The length of the pulse and the period of its repetition depend mainly on the

transformer characteristics and the values of the capacitive and resistive timing components. Applications include vertical deflection circuits in televisions, timing circuits in radar and oscilloscopes, frequency dividers and clock oscillators.

A simple sawtooth oscillator is obtained by alternately charging a capacitor through a resistor from a dc voltage supply, and then quickly discharging it. The sawtooth oscillations appear across the capacitor. As long as the voltage range over which the capacitor is charged is less than one tenth of the dc supply voltage, the sawtooth wave is fairly linear. The period of the wave can be altered by changing the value of the capacitor or resistor, or the voltage range over which the capacitor charges.

In the simple arrangement described, because the supply voltage is opposed by the increasing capacitor voltage as it is charged, the charging current through the resistor is correspondingly reduced. Consequently the capacitor is not charged at a constant rate and the sawtooth waveform is not linear. This problem is overcome by charging the capacitor not from a constant voltage source (the dc voltage supply) but from a constant current source. In this way the current into the capacitor is constant regardless of the capacitor voltage.

As time bases, sawtooth oscillators find applications in radar, television, OSCILLOSCOPES, modulation and time measuring equipment, and computers.

Microwave oscillators At frequencies higher than about 1000 MHz, conventional low frequency valves and resonant circuits become inefficient. Most MICROWAVE components and equipment therefore take a different form, for example a resistor is replaced by an attenuator, an LC tuned circuit by a resonator, and a connecting wire or cable by a

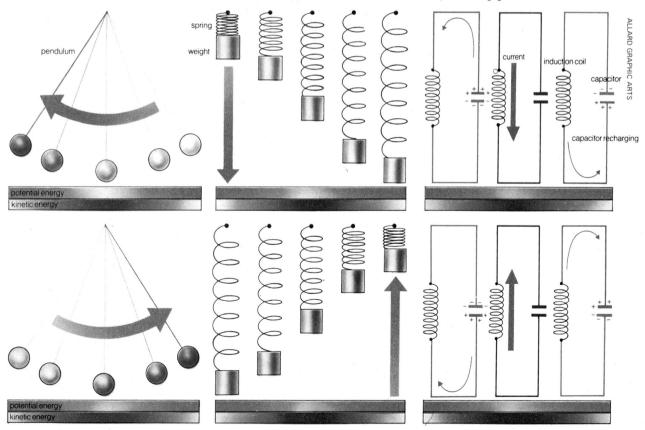

waveguide. The cavity magnetron is a notable example of a microwave oscillator.

The cavity magnetron consists of a cathode surrounded by a cylindrical anode with resonant cavities on its inner face. Switching on the oscillator shocks these cavities into resonance. Electrons travelling towards the anode from the cathode through the perpendicular magnetic and electrostatic fields interact with the fringing field of the resonator slots and give up some of their energy to maintain oscillations in the cavities. Output is taken from one of the cavities by a small coupling loop.

Applications of microwave oscillators range from radio astronomy, communications and television relay networks, radar and navigational aids, to the cooking of food.

In recent years a new two-terminal semiconductor microwave generator has been developed, known as the *Gunn device*. It is essentially a wafer of n-type gallium arsenide. When a low dc voltage of the correct polarity is connected, a dc current flows upon which are superimposed current pulses. These current pulses occur at intervals of the order of 10^{-10} seconds and are used to induce oscillations in a cavity or waveguide resonator. The frequency of the pulses depends on the thickness of the n-type gallium.

The need for smaller and smaller resonant cavities and waveguides to generate the higher microwave frequencies sets an upper practical frequency limit of about 300,000 MHz that may be attained using such techniques. By resort to subatomic techniques, however, microwave frequencies beyond this limit can be generated by using masers, while frequencies in the infra-red and visible portion of the electromagnetic spectrum can be obtained using lasers (see LASER AND MASER).

OSCILLOSCOPE

The oscilloscope is an extremely versatile ELECTRONIC instrument used to display the variations of a physical quantity in time. The 'physical quantity' could be, for example, pressure variations in a circuit or seismic vibrations. They are used in industry, laboratories and for educational purposes in universities and schools.

Working principles The essential components of an oscilloscope include a CATHODE RAY TUBE (CRT) for displaying the waveform or trace, an AMPLIFIER and a *time base*.

Firstly, a fine spot is focused on the CRT screen. This spot is then moved horizontally by means of the time base circuit which is connected to the horizontal deflection plates (called the X-plates) of the CRT. This makes the spot sweep across the screen at a constant speed which can be selected from a range of speeds. The sweep is from left to right and on reaching the right hand side of the screen it 'jumps' back to the left while momentarily reducing the spot intensity so that the jump is not seen. The sweep is then repeated.

The signal to be displayed is fed via an amplifier to the vertical deflection plates (the Y-plates) of the CRT so that the spot is moved up and down as it sweeps across the screen. The observed *trace* corresponds to the fluctuations of the signal in time. The system is similar to a PEN RECORDER except that it is not the 'paper' (screen) that moves but the 'pen' (spot).

Time base circuitry The time base circuit is a sawtooth OSCILLATOR which produces a triangular voltage wave form. The slope of this waveform should be constant—that is, increase linearly with time. When this signal is fed to the X-plates a linearly increasing electric FIELD is generated between the plates which deflects the electron across the screen

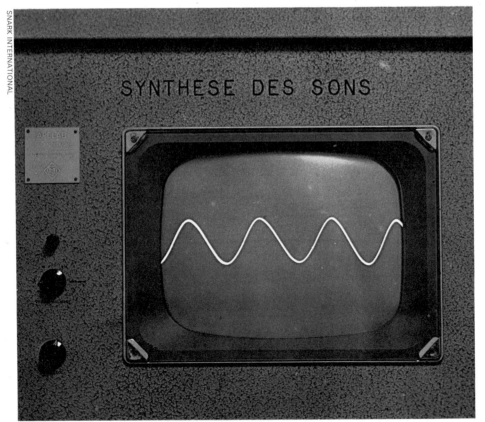

SYNTHESE DES SONS

Left: oscilloscope used in the synthesis of sounds. The waveform shown on the screen is a sinusoidal oscillation.

Right: basic scheme of an oscilloscope showing input signal amplifier, delay line, synchronizing trigger, timebase generator and cathode ray tube (CRT). It is essential for the timebase scanning circuit to be synchronized to the signal input; otherwise the trace drifts across the screen, making observation and measurement difficult. A delay line is often incorporated in oscilloscopes which have facilities for two independent traces to be displayed. Delaying one trace enables comparison of shape and so on to be made. With storage scopes, a trace can be retained for long periods. This works on the principle that a trace leaves the screen positively charged. When the screen is subsequently 'flooded' with low energy electrons, they are attracted to these areas.

in a likewise linear fashion.

By controlling the repetition rate (frequency) of the saw-tooth oscillations the horizontal sweep can be made to match the type of signal under observation. When the signal is non-periodic, just one sweep is required. This is because if several sweeps were to take place successively the resulting image would be confused or 'blurred'. The trace must then be held long enough to be analysed (normally between one and two seconds) and this is achieved by using a high persistence material on the screen.

When, however, the signal has a periodic structure (that is, a shape which is repeated over and over again) it is useful to *synchronize* this signal to the sweep of the time base circuitry.

Synchronization

Without synchronization, it would be impossible to match perfectly the repetition rate of the signal to that of the time base. The resulting trace tends to drift across the screen and is difficult to observe.

To overcome this problem a synchronizing circuit (or *sync* for short) is attached to the time base. This generates a pulse at one particular point of the signal which triggers the time base circuit to produce one sweep. At the end of the sweep the time base is ready to receive another pulse from the sync.

Left: an oscilloscope showing controls. The signal to be displayed is fed to the 'vertical input' (bottom left) and adjusted in magnitude by the 'vertical attenuator' and 'vertical gain' controls (middle left). The timebase (horizontal sweep) frequency is adjusted approximately using the 'horizontal frequency selector' and finely with the 'frequency vernier' (mid centre). Synchronization of the timebase to the signal is achieved using 'external sync' and 'sync selector'. Other controls are brilliance, focus and positioning.

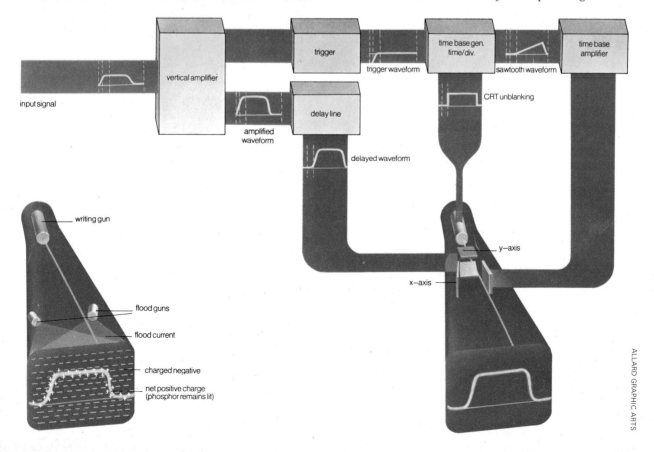

Because the time base is triggered by the same point at every repetition of the signal, the resulting trace is steady and does not drift.

Modifications Sometimes there is a need to display more than one signal at a time—maybe for reasons of comparison. One way of achieving this is to sweep alternately at two different vertical positions with suitable circuitry to direct the correct signal to the correct sweep. With a high persistence CRT the two traces appear to be simultaneous. Another method is to rapidly switch between the two traces in one sweep but this can only be used for signals which are slow compared to the switching rate.

When multiple traces are required the electron beam is initially split into the required number of beams. All are controlled by the same time base circuit and so move across the screen together. Modern oscilloscopes of this form have upwards of four separate traces.

Some oscilloscopes also have storage facilities so that a trace can be viewed at some later time. One way of achieving this is by using an *electrostatic storage tube*. The original trace across the screen leaves the fluorescent material with a positive charge where the trace has passed. Mounted in the CRT is a 'flood gun' and when the trace is to be reproduced the whole screen is flooded with a low energy electron beam. Where the material is positively charged more electrons will be attracted and the glow in these regions is greater than elsewhere thus reproducing the original trace. The trace is erased by using a high energy flow beam. There are other storage techniques also in use including one which uses variable presistence materials.

Lissajous' patterns One facility usually provided is a separate X-plate input. The time base circuit is disconnected and an external signal can be applied to the horizontal plates. When two related signals are fed to the X and Y plates, *Lissajous' patterns* are produced. For example, two sinusoidal waveforms of the same frequency but one 90° out of phase with the other will produce a circle or ellipse on the screen.

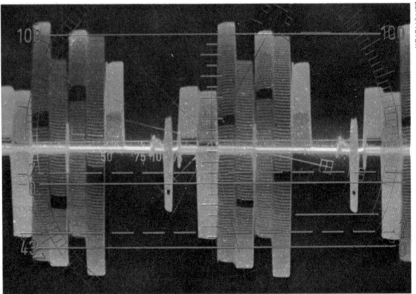

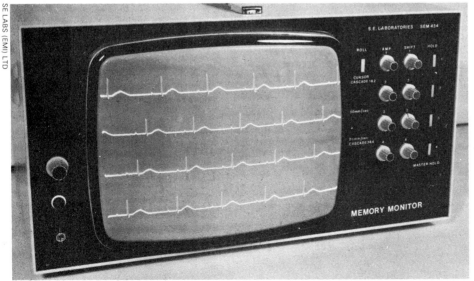

Top left: a Lissajous pattern. This particular pattern is created by using two sine waves with the one going to the vertical plates at half the frequency of the sine wave going to the horizontal plates.

Above: oscilloscopes are often fitted with illuminated scales and grids so that measurements of waveforms can be easily made. Illumination is variable.

Left: with multiple trace oscilloscopes, waveforms from different parts of a system can be monitored simultaneously. This oscilloscope also has a memory unit so that comparisons with earlier signals can be made.

OSMOSIS

If two solutions having different concentrations are separated from each other by a permeable membrane, it is sometimes found that the solvent (the dissolving liquid) molecules will pass through the membrane more quickly than the solute (the dissolved substance) molecules. The result is that solvent passes from the less concentrated solution to the more concentrated one, tending to equalize the concentrations. This process is called *osmosis*.

The phenomenon was discovered by the French physicist Abbé Jean Antoine Nollet in 1748. He covered the wide end of a glass tube with parchment paper and filled the tube with a solution of sucrose (a type of sugar) in water so that it reached a mark on a glass stem drawn out from the other end of the tube. When the covered end of the tube was immersed in a beaker of water, the level of the solution in the stem rose because the water molecules in the beaker were diffusing through the parchment membrane more rapidly than the sucrose molecules leaving the glass tube by the same route. The rise in the solution level in the glass stem created a *hydrostatic* pressure (see STATICS) which was subsequently termed *osmotic pressure*, and is a measure of the pressure caused by the migration of water through the membrane. Since the parchment membrane in Nollet's experiment was slightly permeable to the sucrose molecules, the osmotic pressure was not permanent and the solution in the stem and the water in the beaker eventually came to the same level. The diffusion of solute molecules through a membrane is called *dialysis*, a process used in artificial KIDNEY machines.

Semipermeable membranes When a membrane is only permeable to solvent molecules it is called a *semipermeable membrane*. In 1877 Wilhelm Pfeffer discovered that a gelatinous precipitate of *copper ferrocyanide*, $Cu_2Fe(CN)_6$, formed on the walls of a porous clay cell exhibited semipermeability to cane sugar solutions, and he was able to achieve osmotic pressures as high as four times atmospheric pressure for a 6% by weight solution.

The membranes surrounding the cells of animal and vegetable tissue frequently exhibit semipermeability. If the outer cells of a plant such as *Tradescantia Discolor* (Wandering Jew) are examined under a microscope it will be seen that the cells are pressed against the cellulose sheath surrounding them. When the cell is placed in a 7.5% sucrose solution, however, the osmotic pressure of the solution is greater than that of the cell sap and water passes out of the cell causing it to contract away from the cellulose sheath. This phenomenon is known as *plasmolysis*, and a similar process occurs in the preservation of jams, where 68% sugar solutions dehydrate the cells of micro-organisms and inactivate them (see FOOD PROCESSING).

Reverse osmosis When a pressure greater than the osmotic pressure is applied to an aqueous solution, water molecules can be driven through a semipermeable membrane. The solution is concentrated and pure water is obtained on the other side of the membrane. The membranes can be formed by precipitating materials such as *zirconium oxide*, ZrO_2, on a porcelain support, but the most popular membrane material is *cellulose acetate*. This type of membrane was first developed for

Above right: pure water running from the membrane-containing tubes of a reverse osmosis device used in desalination.

Right: the level of the sugar solution in an inverted funnel rises by osmosis as water passes through a membrane at its lower end.

the DESALINATION of brackish waters and consisted of a skin 0.0001 to 0.0003 mm (0.000004 to 0.000012 inch) thick supported on a permeable substrate 0.04 to 0.09 mm (0.0016 to 0.004 inch) thick reinforced with paper. The skin has a pore size of a few tenths of an angstrom (0.0000001 mm), and water flow rates of up to 50 gallons per day per square foot of membrane (102 litres per hour per square metre) can be achieved.

Cellulose acetate membranes can be used at temperatures from 4°C (39°F) to 60°C (140°F), and they must be chemically sterilized if they are to be used for concentrating biological or food materials. One important use of reverse osmosis is in the concentration of cheese whey. About 30% of the nutritive value of milk is lost in the whey, which contains about 7% dissolved solids. These dissolved solids consist mainly of lactose but also contain from 0.5 to 1.0% protein and about 1% of lactic acid and other salts. The whey is first passed through an 'open' membrane which retains the protein fraction for subsequent spray drying. The filtrate from this stage then passes to a 'tight' membrane where mainly lactose is retained. The water and some of the dissolved salts are discharged after passing through the membrane. The process not only recovers valuable food sources but also reduces the polluting effect of cheese whey.

Reverse osmosis, which is sometimes known as *ultrafiltration* or *hyperfiltration* depending on the degree of solute and solvent separation, has also been applied to the concentration of sugar beet extract, skimmed milk, enzymes and polio vaccines.

Osmotic dehydration Recently methods have been developed to preserve fruits by a combination of osmosis and dehydration by fluidized bed, vacuum or freeze drying. The method has been successfully applied to apple slices which have first been *blanched* to inactivate the enzymes (see FOOD PRESERVA-

TION). The apple slices are immersed in a bath of sucrose syrup at a concentration of about 70% by weight and a temperature of from 60°C (140°F) to 65°C (149°F). The syrup is circulated in the bath by a pump to avoid dilution at the fruit surface and thus maintain the osmotic pressure. After four to six hours approximately 40% of the apple slice weight has been lost by migration of water from the fruit by osmosis, and the apples are then washed to remove sucrose syrup from the fruit surface. Final drying is achieved in a vacuum oven at 60°C (140°F) and a pressure of about 13 psi (0.9 bar).

MILK MARKETING BOARD

Above: separating protein from cheese whey by ultrafiltration. The whey is pressed under pressure through a series of porous tubes lined with cellulose membranes which retain the protein.

Below: an experiment to demonstrate osmosis. A container is divided into two compartments by a semipermeable membrane and one is filled with water while the other is filled with a salt solution. To begin with, the liquid levels are the same (left), but water soon passes through the membrane and into the salt solution (right).

ALLARD GRAPHIC ARTS

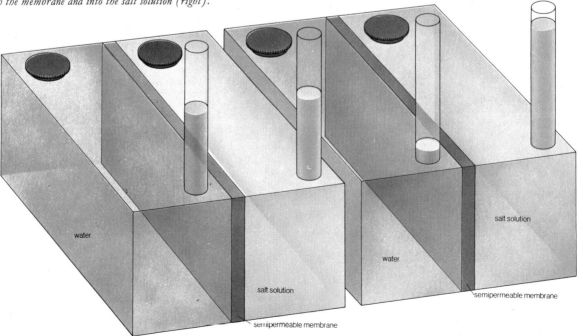

OUTBOARD MOTOR

An outboard motor is a basically self-contained power unit for small boats and dinghies which is clamped to the *transom* (stern) of the craft. The earliest outboard motors appeared at the beginning of this century, the first being a French design, the Motogodille, in 1902. In the mid-1900s Cameron Waterman in the USA produced a small outboard, but it was Ole Evinrude, a Norwegian-American living in Milwaukee, who produced the first commercially successful design which went into production in 1909 after about three years of development.

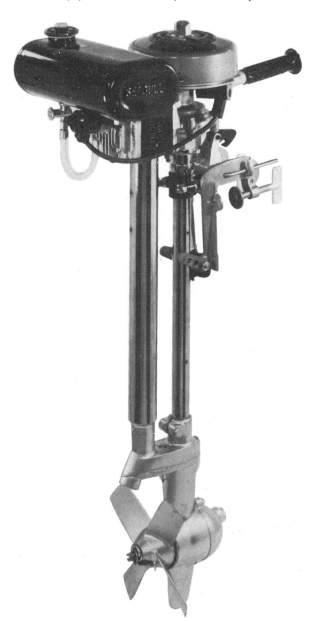

Above: a typical lightweight outboard motor unit. The propeller is locked on to the drive shaft by means of a shearing pin, so that if the propeller gets jammed by an underwater obstruction the pin will shear. This prevents damage to the transmission and propeller.

Right: a Johnson rotary outboard engine used on racing boats.

The powerhead The unit containing the engine, electrical system, and on smaller motors the fuel tank, is called the *powerhead*. Almost all outboard motors have two-stroke petrol [gasoline] engines (see INTERNAL COMBUSTION ENGINE), although some are four-stroke (such as the Fisher-Pierce Bearcat), and small electric-powered motors are available. The first WANKEL powered outboard motor was the Mac 10, with a single rotor Sachs-Wankel KM48 engine of 160 cc (9.8 cu in) capacity giving 9.5 bhp at 4800 revs/min, and many companies are now developing rotary engined outboards.

The cylinders are usually horizontal, with the drive being taken from the lower end of the vertical crankshaft by a transmission shaft that drives the PROPELLER via the GEARBOX and propeller shaft, which are housed in the underwater unit. Ignition is by MAGNETO on the smaller motors, but many modern high power motors use electronic IGNITION SYSTEMS in conjunction with an ALTERNATOR.

Most outboards are water cooled, the cooling water being drawn in by an impeller in the lower (underwater) unit and circulated around the engine before being expelled through ports at the rear above the propeller.

A wide range of power outputs is available, from about 1 bhp to 135 bhp or more. The smaller motors are started by a starting cord wound round the flywheel, but most motors above about 5 or 6 bhp have electric starters as standard or optional equipment, often with a starting cord provided for emergency starting.

Engine exhaust is usually discharged underwater through a submerged outlet port, and some types discharge the exhaust through the propeller hub.

Lower unit The lower unit houses the gearbox, gearchange mechanism, propeller shaft, and the cooling water

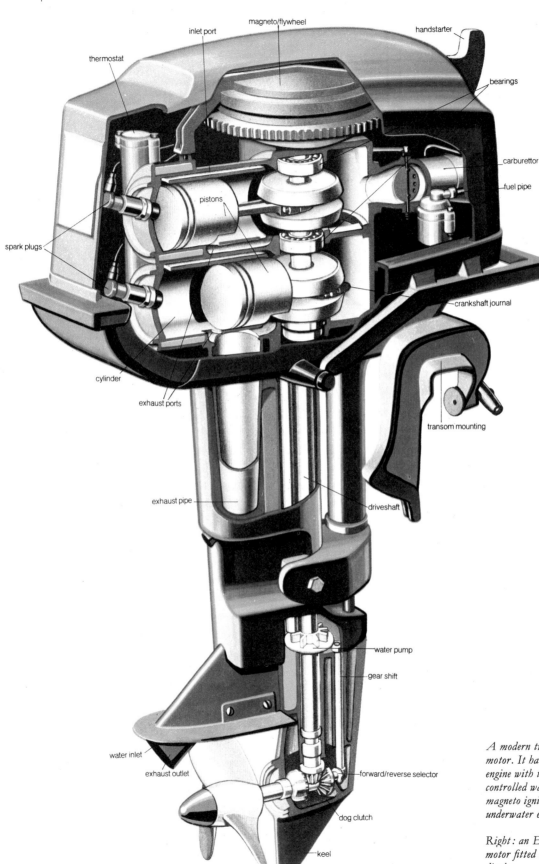

JOHN BISHOP

thermostat

inlet port

magneto/flywheel

handstarter

bearings

carburettor

fuel pipe

pistons

spark plugs

crankshaft journal

cylinder

exhaust ports

transom mounting

exhaust pipe

driveshaft

water pump

gear shift

water inlet

exhaust outlet

forward/reverse selector

dog clutch

keel

*A modern two cylinder outboard
motor. It has a two-stroke
engine with thermostatically
controlled water cooling,
magneto ignition, and an
underwater exhaust outlet.*

*Right: an Evinrude outboard
motor fitted to an inflatable
dinghy*

impeller, except on the smallest motors which have no gearchange, reversing being achieved by turning the motor right round so that the propeller acts in the reverse direction. The gearbox has forward, neutral, and reverse gears, selected either by a mechanical linkage from the gearlever or on some models by a SOLENOID unit.

The rotation of the propeller tends to turn the boat, that is, if the propeller is turning clockwise (viewed from the rear) it will tend to drive the rear of the boat towards the right, and the boat will self-steer towards the left (port). On many outboards this tendency is counteracted by a small fixed RUDDER, the *trim rudder*, mounted above the propeller. This trim rudder also serves to reduce the amount of electrolytic corrosion of the propeller caused by the action of salt water on the propeller and adjacent metalwork. If the propeller is made of bronze and the trim rudder of zinc, the electrolytic action will erode the relatively cheap and easily replaceable trim rudder but not the more expensive bronze propeller. On many modern outboards the propellers are of plastic material or plastic coated stainless steel, so electrolytic corrosion of the propeller is not a problem (see also ELECTROLYSIS and CORROSION PREVENTION).

Control Small engines are usually steered by a tiller type steering handle, and engine speed is controlled by a throttle lever mounted on the steering handle or by a twistgrip control at the end of the handle. Gearchange is by means of a gearlever mounted on the powerhead.

On engines with higher power outputs this arrangement is unsatisfactory, as it may be almost impossible to steer the craft when the engine is producing about 20 bhp or more. For these motors (and when more than one motor is fitted) the steering is by cables linked to a steering wheel, and the gearchange and throttle are operated by levers connected to the motor by cable links. Some motors use a single lever for both throttle and gears. When the lever is in its midway position the gearbox is in neutral and the engine is idling. As the lever is moved forward, forward gear is selected, and further movement of the lever opens the throttle. To reverse, the lever is moved back through its midway position (so the engine is idled and the gears put in neutral), and further movement backwards changes the gears into reverse and then opens the throttle again.

When two levers are used, one for throttle and one for gears, there is usually a safety interlock so that the gears cannot be changed unless the throttle lever is in the idling position. If two or more engines are used to drive a boat, a single cable-linked lever arrangement is used for each engine, with the levers mounted next to each other near the steering wheel so that they can be operated simultaneously with one hand.

OXIDATION and REDUCTION

Oxidation and reduction are chemical terms describing particular types of chemical reactions. As the understanding of the electronic structure of the ATOM and the changes which took place in chemical reactions developed, the definition of these terms also changed. Originally oxidation meant the combination of a chemical ELEMENT with OXYGEN to form an oxide; reduction meant the removal from a compound of all or part of the oxygen it contained. Some important chemical processes can be understood in terms of this simple definition.

Combustion or burning is probably the most familiar of all chemical reactions. Most of the common fuels (petroleum, gas, coal, wood) are complex compounds containing CARBON. On ignition they react with the oxygen of the air to form a mixture of oxides, carbon monoxide, CO, and carbon dioxide, CO_2, and these can thus be described as oxidation processes. Combustion is not confined to carbon fuels. Many metals when heated in air also combine with the oxygen of the air to form the oxide: for example, at red heat elemental copper is converted to black copper oxide.

$$2\,Cu\ +\ O_2\ \rightarrow 2CuO$$
copper   oxygen   copper oxide

The most common reduction reaction in terms of this simple definition is the smelting of iron ore. It is probably one of the oldest industrial processes having been carried out for over four thousand years. Iron is widely distributed in the Earth's crust usually in the form of *limonite*, *haematite* and *magnetite*, all of which are oxides of iron. Originally the metal was extracted

Below: the copper dome of the Library of Congress in Washington, DC. Copper is oxidized very slowly by the atmosphere to a basic carbonate which gives the dome its characteristic green colour.

by heating a mixture of charcoal and iron ore to very high temperatures and blasting air through the mixture. The iron ore was converted to molten metal, which on cooling could be separated from the charcoal ash. With the replacement of charcoal by coke in the eighteenth century, the BLAST FURNACE was developed. The main reaction occurring in a blast furnace is the reduction of the iron oxide, Fe_2O_3, by carbon monoxide. The carbon monoxide is oxidized to carbon dioxide. In general, oxidation and reduction occur simultaneously and in equivalent amounts during any reaction involving either process:

$$Fe_2O_3 + 3CO \rightarrow 2Fe + 3CO_2$$
iron oxide carbon monoxide iron carbon dioxide

Because oxygen reacts so readily with HYDROGEN to form water, the latter was considered to be the chemical opposite of oxygen. The concept of oxidation was thus extended to the loss of hydrogen from a compound, and reduction to the gain of hydrogen by a compound. For example, in the reaction of hydrogen sulphide, H_2S, and CHLORINE, Cl_2, to form hydrogen chloride, HCl, and SULPHUR, S, the hydrogen sulphide is oxidized and the chlorine is reduced.

$$H_2S + Cl_2 \rightarrow 2HCl + S$$
hydrogen sulphide chlorine hydrogen chloride sulphur

Electronic theory

When oxygen reacts with other elements it acts as an ELECTRON acceptor, in other words it gains electrons from the combining element. Thus the process of *oxidation* involves *electron loss*. The concept of oxidation has therefore been extended to include all processes in which electron loss occurs irrespective of whether oxygen is involved or not. Thus in the reaction of magnesium with chlorine, the magnesium is oxidized to magnesium chloride; the neutral magnesium atom is converted to the positively charged magnesium ION, Mg^{++}.

$$Mg + Cl_2 \rightarrow MgCl_2$$
magnesium chlorine magnesium chloride

Or in the reaction of ferrous chloride with chlorine, the ferrous ion, Fe^{++}, which has a positive charge of two is oxidized to the ferric ion, Fe^{+++}, which has a positive charge of three.

$$2 FeCl_2 + Cl_2 \rightarrow 2 FeCl_3$$
ferrous chloride chlorine ferric chloride

When oxygen is removed from an oxide the combining element gains electrons, for example in the reduction of copper oxide by hydrogen the positively charged copper ion, Cu^{++} is reduced to the neutral copper atom, Cu. Thus *reduction* is synonymous with *electron gain* and an increase in *electronegative* character. In fact the generalized concept of reduction includes all such reactions in which there is a net increase in electronegative character by the reacting species. Thus a ferric chloride solution will react with hydrogen sulphide to give ferrous chloride, hydrogen chloride and sulphur.

$$2 FeCl_3 + H_2S \rightarrow 2 FeCl_2 + HCl + S$$
ferric chloride hydrogen sulphide ferrous chloride hydrogen chloride sulphur

The ferric ion with a positive charge of $3+$ is reduced to the ferrous ion with a positive charge of $2+$.

Oxidation and reduction reactions

These broad definitions of oxidation and reduction cover a wide range of chemical reactions including some important industrial and natural process. All electrolytic processes can be interpreted as oxidation and reduction reactions. IN ELECTROLYSIS, the *cation* (the positively charged electrolytic species) gains electrons at the cathode, and the process can therefore be described as reduction. At the anode, on the other hand, the *anion* (the negatively charged electrolytic species) gives up electrons. This process can be described as oxidation. In the electrolysis of sodium chloride the chloride ions, Cl^-, are oxidized at the anode to form chlorine, and the sodium ions, Na^+ are reduced at the cathode to form elemental sodium.

Another common process which can be classified as an oxidation reaction is the CORROSION of metals. The rusting of iron is one of the most common examples of oxidation. Indeed the final fate of most iron and steel articles is to be destroyed by rust. There are certain conditions necessary before rusting can take place; both moisture and oxygen must be present, and there must be an *electropositive* area in the metal (formed by an

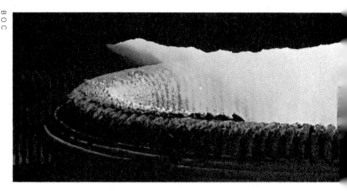

Above: pure oxygen is blown into a steelmaking furnace to remove impurities such as carbon, silicon and phosphorus by oxidation. Large amounts of heat are released during this process.

impurity or scratch on the surface). The corrosion process can be compared to an electrolytic cell in which the electropositive area acts as an anode and the undamaged area acts as a cathode. Iron atoms are oxidized at the anode and go into solution as ferrous ions, Fe^{++}. The released electrons flow to the cathode where hydroxyl ions, OH^-, are formed from the cathode area. The ferrous ions and hydroxyl ions diffuse into the water or react with the oxygen in air forming $Fe_2O_3.3H_2O$, or rust.

Some physiological processes can be explained in terms of oxidation and reduction. For example the method by which the human body obtains energy and heat from food is basically an oxidation reaction. The process of digestion enables food to be absorbed by the blood stream. On passing through the lungs the blood stream acquires oxygen which combines loosely with the haemoglobin of the blood and oxidizes the food to form carbon dioxide and water.

OXY-ACETYLENE WELDING (see welding)

Below: one of the most common examples of oxidation is the corrosion of metals. The picture shows a pile of rusted scrap iron sheets which will be used to make fresh steel.

OXYGEN

The discovery of oxygen, chemical symbol O_2, and the development of the modern theory of combustion were milestones in the history of science. These discoveries established chemistry as a modern science clearly divorced from ALCHEMY. Although the ancient Greek and Arab philosophers were vaguely aware of some connection between air and combustion and life, no major discovery in this field occurred until the late eighteenth century.

On 1 August 1774 Joseph Priestley examined the effect of intense heat on mercuric oxide. He noted that an air or gas was readily expelled from the specimen. To his surprise a candle burned in this with a remarkably vigorous flame. He called this new substance 'dephlogisticated air' in terms of the current chemical theory of combustion (see PHLOGISTON). On a visit to Paris in 1775 he related his discovery directly to LAVOISIER. Immediately Lavoisier checked the results by accurate experiments and found that Priestley's dephlogisticated air combined with metals and other substances. Since some of the compounds he formed produced acids he regarded the dephlogisticated air as an acidifying principle and called it *oxygine* derived from the Greek words for 'sour' and 'I produce'.

About the same time a Swedish apothecary named Scheele had been carrying out researches similar to Priestley's. He had discovered and identified a gas which he called 'fire air'; it was oxygen. He did not publish his results, however, until 1777, and the discovery of oxygen has therefore been attributed to Priestley.

From his experiments Lavoisier recognized that air was composed of two main constituents: 'vital air' or oxygen and 'azote' (Greek for 'lifeless'—now called NITROGEN) which would not support life or combustion. From these facts Lavoisier developed the modern theory of combustion, and thus laid the foundation of modern chemistry.

Manufacture Originally oxygen was prepared on an industrial scale by the Brin process. Barium oxide, BaO, is heated in compressed air to form barium peroxide, BaO_2. The temperature and pressure are reduced and the peroxide reverts to the monoxide. During this process, oxygen is released.

$$2BaO_2 \rightarrow 2BaO + O_2$$

barium peroxide   barium oxide   oxygen

Today a little oxygen is prepared by the electrolytic decomposition of water, but the principal method of production is the liquefaction and fractional DISTILLATION of air. In a typical air liquefaction plant there are three fundamental processes: air purification, partial liquefaction of the air using HEAT EXCHANGERS and separation into oxygen and nitrogen by fractional distillation. Air is compressed to 150 times atmospheric pressure and passed through a carbon dioxide removal unit and a moisture removal unit. It then enters the heat exchanger where the temperature is reduced to $-170°C$ ($-274°F$). The cold nitrogen from the column is used in the heat exchanger. Some of the cold air is fed to an *expansion engine* where it is made to do work, thus reducing the temperature of the air as energy is removed. It rejoins the rest of the cold air from the heat exchanger and enters a high pressure column where it is fractionated to a stream of almost pure nitrogen and an oxygen rich stream.

The nitrogen from the high pressure column is condensed in a condenser—reboiler, and is used as a *reflux* stream in the low pressure column. The oxygen rich air stream is drawn off the high pressure column and fed into the low pressure column, where it is fractionated. Both nitrogen and oxygen are drawn off from the low pressure column.

Uses By far the largest industrial use of oxygen is in steel-making (see IRON and STEEL MANUFACTURE). Recent new processes introduced in the steel industry depend on a huge and constant supply of oxygen. Instead of using an air blast from the base of the furnace, an oxygen blast at 10 times atmospheric pressure is applied over the top of the white hot cast iron. This process produces a better type of steel because no nitrogen is present. Another important commerical application for oxygen is in the cutting of ferrous (iron-containing) metals into shapes for fabrication. In this technique the metal is heated by means of a fuel-oxygen flame to the point of combustion and then a high speed stream of oxygen is fed to the centre of the flame. The metal burns and melts leaving a narrow cut. Oxy-acetylene WELDING has been widely used since the beginning of the century. Acetylene in the presence of oxygen produces a high temperature flame which will melt most metals, allowing them to be welded together.

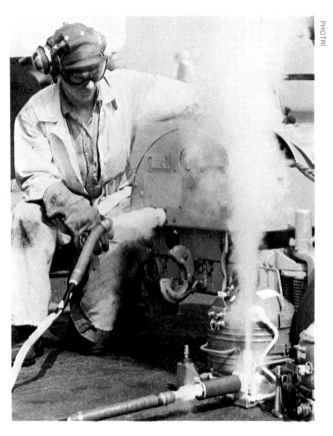

Up to a height of 14 miles (22 km) above the surface of the Earth, the proportion of oxygen in the atmosphere remains constant at 20.9%. However, the atmospheric pressure and the partial pressure of oxygen decrease rapidly. Therefore, in high flying aircraft, although the aircraft is pressurized, an emergency supply of oxygen is provided. In deep-sea diving at depths greater than 250 ft (76.2 m) compressed air cannot be used because of the formation of nitrogen bubbles in the diver's circulatory system (air contains approximately 78% nitrogen). Neither can pure oxygen be used because prolonged exposure produces toxic effects. Mixtures of oxygen and the INERT GAS helium, however, have been found to be suitable for respiration at these depths.

Almost all hospitals now have piped installations providing oxygen to wards and operating theatres. Oxygen tents are used frequently for patients with respiratory difficulties, and in anaesthesia oxygen is mixed with the anaesthetic gas, for example nitrous oxide, halothane or cyclopropane, to ensure an adequate supply for life support (see ANAESTHETIC MACHINES).

In the aerospace industry liquid oxygen is the most commonly used oxidant in rocket propulsion. The oxygen and the fuel (usually kerosene) are fed under pressure into the thrust chamber where they are mixed and burned at high pressures. The gaseous reaction products are accelerated and ejected at high velocities, thus providing the propulsive thrust.

Oxides Since the atmosphere contains 20.9% by volume of oxygen, and since it is capable of reacting with most elements other than the inert gases, it is not surprising that oxides are widely distributed in nature. The most common and the one having the most vital importance to life is water, H_2O, which was once thought to be an element. Without it life on earth would not exist, because it plays an essential part in the physiological processes of both plants and animals. Pure water, however, does not exist in nature. Its purity varies according to its source; sea water can have dissolved salts at concentrations as high as 3.5%. Although its chemical formula is H_2O, pure water is really a polymeric material (see POLYMER) better represented as $(H_2O)_n$, n being a large number, in which the individual molecules are linked together through their hydrogen atoms by chemical BONDS called *hydrogen bonds*. The exact structure of the pure water polymer has been a subject of controversy for many years. Compared to similar chemical compounds water has unusual physical properties; its boiling point, 100°C (212°F), and melting point 0°C (32°F) are higher

Left: a flight deck crewman on the USS Enterprise pumps liquid oxygen from a storage tank into small portable units used to fill aircraft systems. The oxygen must pass through pressure reduction and heating devices before pilots can breathe it. Vaporized oxygen is allowed to escape to prevent a dangerous build up of pressure.

Below: highly concentrated hydrogen peroxide is used as a rocket fuel; it readily decomposes into water in the form of steam, and oxygen. Because concentrated hydrogen peroxide is both explosive and toxic, it must be handled with great care.

Right: the distillation columns of an air liquefaction plant. Nowadays oxygen is prepared almost exclusively by liquefying air and separating it into its components, mainly oxygen and nitrogen, by fractional distillation.

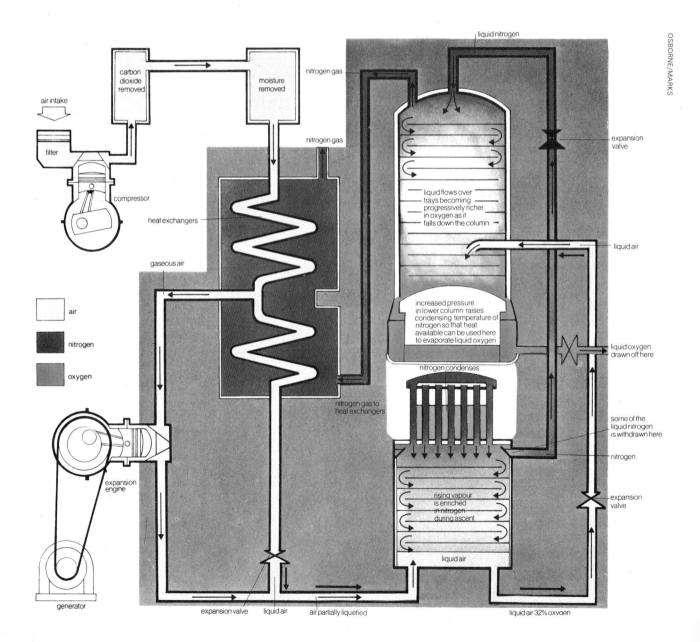

than would be predicted from this comparison. These unusual properties can only be explained in terms of its polymeric structure.

The second oxide of hydrogen in which two atoms of oxygen are combined with two atoms of hydrogen, H_2O_2, is called hydrogen peroxide. This compound which has been known for more than 150 years is not very stable in the pure state; it decomposes easily to form water and oxygen. On an industrial scale, it is prepared by the ELECTROLYSIS of *ammonium hydrogen sulphate*, NH_4HSO_4, using a PLATINUM anode and a LEAD cathode. Because of its instability in the pure state, hydrogen peroxide is usually used in dilute aqueous solution. It decomposes to form water and oxygen, and is therefore a powerful oxidizing agent (see OXIDATION and REDUCTION). It is widely used both domestically and industrially for bleaching purposes; it oxidizes dyes to colourless substance without damaging the fabric or fibre being bleached.

Many of the industrially important metals including iron exist in nature as their oxides. The pure metals are obtained by a process known as *reduction*. Iron is the second most abundant metal in the Earth's crust and is certainly the most important. Even though it is obtainable from its oxides, in the presence of air and moisture it slowly reverts to its oxide. This is the familiar process known as rusting.

Ozone
Ozone, O_3, is an allotrope of oxygen, in other words it is the same element existing in a different form. Structurally the difference between the two compounds is that oxygen has two atoms per MOLECULE whereas ozone has three.

Chemically the properties of these two compounds are very different. A simple example of this difference is their effect on human respiration: oxygen is essential for respiration to take place, whereas ozone at concentrations greater than 1 part per million is toxic to man. Ozone occurs naturally in the atmosphere at very low concentrations (0.03 part per million), although in the stratosphere there is an ozone layer which is formed by the action of short wavelength radiation from the Sun on oxygen. This ozone layer is vital for human life, for its absorbs radiation which would be fatal to man.

Ozone is usually prepared by passing a silent electric discharge through oxygen. Concentrations up to 5% of ozone in oxygen can be prepared by this manner. Because of its powerful oxidizing properties ozone is widely used for sterilizing water and for air purification purposes. It also finds applications in organic chemistry in *ozonolysis*, which is the reaction of ozone with unsaturated compounds such as the HYDROCARBON ethylene.

OZONE (see oxygen)

PACEMAKER (HEART) (see heart pacemaker)

COLORIFIC/NASA

Above left: oxygen is pumped into a gravel pit to reduce the effect of polluting chemicals. Enrichment of the water with oxygen ensures the continued survival of fish and other aquatic life forms.

Left: oxygen is produced by the liquefaction and distillation of air. The air is first compressed and then cooled in the first heat exchanger. The pressure is released in driving the expansion engine and the air is partially liquefied. It then passes to a distillation column where it is separated into liquid oxygen and nitrogen.

Right: the lift-off of Apollo 11. The first stage of the Saturn V rocket uses liquid oxygen and kerosene as fuel while the second stage uses liquid oxygen and liquid hydrogen.

PACKAGING

The design and operation of packaging machinery involves chemistry, ERGONOMIC DESIGN, computers for AUTOMATIC CONTROL, and many other branches of art and science. A package may be a slender glass ampoule containing a product for injection, filled and sealed in a sterile atmosphere, a catheter sealed in a plastic bag and sterilized ready for use *after* the bag is sealed, or it may be a softwood crate in which an automobile is shipped across oceans. Between these extremes are millions of bags, bottles, cartons, tubes, injection moulded (see PLASTICS) or thermo-formed plastic 'nests' and so forth. As an anti-pilferage precaution, small items for sale in self-service shops are displayed inside plastic 'blisters' sealed to the surface of large cards. It is now common for the customer to carry away not just a package but a package of packages, for example a carton of bottles of soft drink.

The slow speed and expense of manual handling, filling, weighing, labelling and so on has caused the development of machinery which does the job faster and faster. Today there are complex automatic packaging systems that take the product and the package from bulk and produce entire pallets of packages, strapped, shrink-wrapped or stretch-wrapped for shipment. The only limitation on the design of packaging machinery is the fact that certain functions, such as weighing, are slower than labelling, for example, which for glass bottles has now exceeded 1000 bottles a minute.

Bottles Bottles are delivered by slat conveyer to smoothly turning plastic spirals that space them into place on individual platforms mounted on a turntable or carousel, which as it turns lifts them (by means of cams) and brings the bottle mouth firmly into contact with injecting nozzles. The entire sequence of events is controlled by fail-safe devices so that if a bottle breaks, the line stops, or if a bottle fails to arrive on its platform, the relevant nozzle does not discharge. The dose from the nozzle is measured volumetrically, by a piston action and suitable valves, or by the turning of an auger in a tube, which permits the handling of semi-liquids and those containing solids in suspension. Drip cut-off devices ensure that the outside of the bottle, and the surface which will accept the cork, cap or other closing device, is not soiled.

Cartons Machinery can insert or construct a bag inside a carton seconds before it is filled, as for example a cereal box. The cartons themselves are withdrawn by the machine from a magazine in a flat state. The suction device that pulls them into the machinery opens them into the rectangular state, the bottom flaps are turned over and tucked in or brushed by a glue wheel and then closed, and the cartons are placed on conveyer mounted flights or paddles, carried in line or on a carousel. A similar top-sealing operation takes place after a checkweigher sees that the fill is present and complete.

Bagging Bags are made from various plastic films, aluminium foil, and *laminates* (materials combined in layers) as

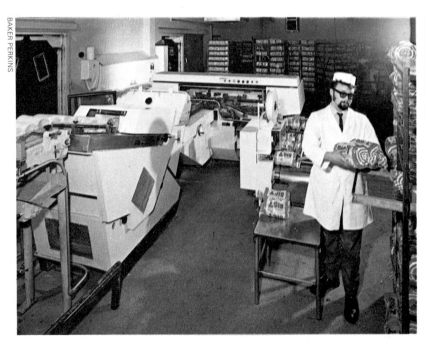

well as paper. The bags are formed by the machinery from a strip of pre-printed material called the web: the pre-printed web is correctly positioned for cut-off by spots or bars which are observed by electronic scanning devices. Bags used for bulk materials are sealed by quick-set ADHESIVES. Where dissimilar materials are used, when paper or board is coated or laminated with polyethylene on one side only, *hot melts* are used which adhere to any surface and cool to seal in seconds.

Some of the most highly developed packages today are the pouches used for powdered soup and similar products. These use paper for its low cost and printability, with aluminium foil on the inside for lightproofness and impermeability, and polyethylene inside that to make a heat seal. The pouches are made from a single printed web of the laminate, fin-sealed around three edges, filled, and closed by applying a heated sealing bar to the pouch mouth.

Other operations
In many cases filling accuracy is demanded by legislation, or involves valuable or even dangerous substances. Today weight filling is an integral part of the packing machinery and can include feedback mechanisms which amend the action of the filling device when the packages coming forward are sensed to be slightly over or under weight.

Bottles and cans (see CAN MANUFACTURE) are *wrapped* nowadays by the machinery in pre-erected containers. The machines use diecut, creased board blanks, wrapping them around a group of cans, bottles or whatever, so tightly that they will not need partitions to prevent the labels from rubbing against each other, and so that their mutual support actually reduces damage in transit. In addition, less board is used than in the older method which allowed for a size tolerance to permit easy loading.

Machinery can code-mark packages with factory location, packing date, *sell-by* date and so forth. A number of sealed cartons, bottles or whatever are collected on a platform from a conveyer and then wrapped, as above, or dropped into a case or a large carton or tray; the sealed units in turn are collected on a pallet. For despatch, individual items or whole pallets can be automatically wrapped in plastic. *Shrink-wrapping* is the use

TETRA PAK

Below left: packaging bread. The machine puts each loaf into a plastic bag and fastens the end with a plastic clip.

Below centre: boxes being filled. After going round the carousel the flaps on the boxes are folded and tucked or brushed with glue.

Below: wrapping cheddar cheese. The wrap is a pre-printed plastic material which is wrapped around the cheese and then heat-sealed on the ends to keep natural moisture in.

Above: a continuous web of pre-printed matter is automatically made into Tetra-Paks, sterilized, filled, cut off and sealed.

DICKINSON ROBINSON GROUP

of a plastic film which is stretched cold around the product; when heat is applied, *plastic memory* causes the film to try to go back to its original shape. *Stretch-wrapping* is almost the same except that the product is pushed through a curtain of film so that the film is stretched around it and the expense of a heat tunnel is dispensed with. Recently Swedish and British engineers have developed methods of stretch-wrapping entire pallet loads, keeping the goods cleaner in transit and holding down pilferage.

Systems The trend in packaging is toward systems sold by companies which design, supply and guarantee the cartons and the machinery. In some cases they offer complicated double-wall cartons that could not be set up, filled and sealed manually. The cartons that contain cigarettes are made up, as are the cigarettes themselves and the triple-layer packets, on integrated systems which also case the cartons in corrugated fibreboard cases.

One of the most highly developed packaging systems is that designed in Sweden for the packaging of milk in the familiar tetrahedral cartons called Tetra-Paks. The package is made from a continuous roll of pre-printed web, which is pulled over forming 'shoulders' on to a metal tube, with a small overlap. By applying heat to the overlap a continuous sealed tube is formed. This is pulled down by two pairs of heated jaws at right-angles to each other. By feeding milk into the top of the metal tube, with the action of the heated metal jaws which press hard enough to force the milk away from the sealing point, a completely full package with the largest possible capacity made from a paperboard tube is created. The machinery has been adapted to make automatically formed, filled and sealed rectangular milk cartons of various sizes.

The next development was the idea of passing the plastic coated web through a bath of hydrogen peroxide just before it is formed into a tube. By then applying the heat in such a way that the liquid is literally burned off, the resulting carton is rendered sterile. If the milk itself is sterile and the whole

Below: cardboard boxes being fabricated. In the magazine at the top the flat stock is stored to be drawn off one piece at a time; the machine folds the pieces and tucks in the flaps; the completed boxes are carried away on a conveyer.

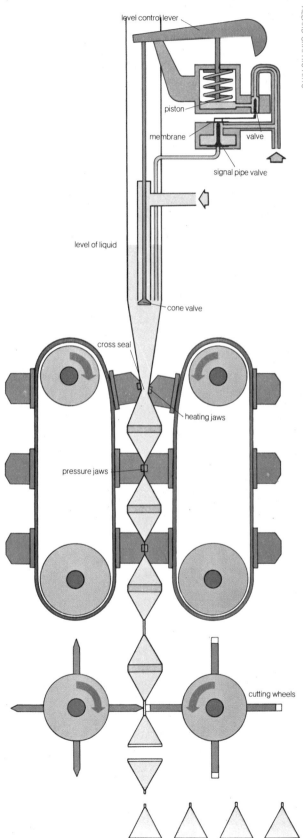

operation done in an enclosed sterile atmosphere, the end product is packaged milk which will keep for long periods without refrigeration. Thus men at sea can enjoy fresh milk all the way, and milk can be stored ahead of time for holiday periods of exceptional demand.

Automated dairy plants are now provided which can receive, empty and return the milk churns, check the milk quality, feed it to the correct machine depending on what shape and size carton is desired, stack the unit packages into automatically erected fibreboard trays or crates, palletize complete loads and shrinkwarp them, with only a few trained engineers in attendance. Each pallet holds 72 cases of aseptically formed milk cartons containing in all 1728 litres of long-life milk.

The idea of using a continuous heat-sealed tube is being exploited for other products. When the tube is formed, chocolate bars or other items can be placed on it, and the process is called flow wrapping because a continuous flow of items is produced. There are vertical machines which produce bags of weighed-out sweets or potato crisps [chips], heat-sealing the web to make the packages; with a weldable plastic like polyethylene, a hot wire passed through the web cuts it off and makes a bead seal on each side.

In another development, the web is heated and stretched by the application of a vacuum into a dish shape that provides a nest for the product. Then a second web is heat-sealed to a flange on the 'dish', completely enclosing the item. A similar technique is used to make the plastic sachets containing shampoo and similar products; two webs, or a single V-folded web, are thermo-formed from PVC and fin-sealed, using high-frequency current to weld the plastic together.

It is not necessary for the packages to be made of similar materials. Provided one or both are heat sealable, a plastic film can be sealed to a printed card to make the familiar 'blister packs'; alternatively, a thin web of plastic film can be heated and drawn down on a heat sensitive card by means of a vacuum, a process described as *skin* wrapping.

All these packaging techniques, and many which have not yet been discovered, are necessary in a society which is oriented to consumption and in which the manual filling, sealing and so forth would be too slow, too expensive and too boring for the people who would have to do it.

Above: pre-printed plastic packaging material for sweets. The machine will deposit a measured weight of sweets on the material, cut it off and seal it all the way round.

Right: packaging biscuits. The packets move along a conveyer and the biscuits come up an elevator; then the packet is sealed.

Left: the machinery which makes the familiar Tetra-Paks, in which the pre-printed material is formed into a tube as it is pulled down past a device operated by compressed air which controls the fluid level in the tube. If the fluid level falls too low, the pressure of the air in the signal pipe falls, operating a series of valves which allow compressed air to act on the piston, which by means of levers pushes the cone valve downward, allowing more fluid to enter the tube. Sealing of the cartons is accomplished by sets of jaws which supply heat on one side and pressure on the other. The diagram shows only one set of jaws and one set of cut-off wheels; there are actually two sets of each, at right angles to one another. Since the cartons are sealed below the level of the liquid they contain no air; they are packaged automatically into returnable or single-service hexagonal transport cases.

PAINT manufacture

The beginnings of the making and use of paint by man go back far into prehistory. The activity probably arose from his desire to decorate the walls of his home with reminders of things he prized. Animals, important as a source of food and skins, have been found depicted in cave dwellings at Lascaux in France and Altamira in Spain.

These paintings were probably produced by smearing the rock with a finger dipped in a rudimentary mixture of coloured earth and water or perhaps animal fat. These simple constituents —coloured powder and fluid carrier—have remained through the ages the essential ingredients of paints.

Paint can be defined as any fluid material that will spread over a solid surface and dry or harden to an adherent and coherent coloured obscuring film. It usually consists of a powdered solid (the *pigment*) suspended in a liquid (the *vehicle*, *medium* or *binder*). The pigment provides the colouring and obscuring properties. The binder is the film-forming component which holds the pigment particles together and attaches them to the surface over which they are spread.

Decoration seems to have been the original purpose of paint, but in time its power to protect the vulnerable surfaces of manmade objects became of almost equal importance. Houses, ships, vehicles, furniture and so on look better and last longer when painted.

Paint systems and types For maximum protection and durability it is necessary to employ a multiple coat system. The first layer of *primer* ensures adhesion between the *substrate* and subsequent coats. Then comes the *undercoat* to obscure what is beneath it and provide a suitable surface for the final coat. Finally there is the *topcoat* or *finish* to give the required appearance as regards colour and gloss. Paints are available to give a full gloss, 'eggshell' or matt finish.

The traditional oil gloss paint was a mixture of linseed oil, pigment, thinning solvent (commonly turpentine) and additives to promote drying. Addition of natural resin to refined and treated linseed oil improved the spreading properties, rate of drying and gloss. The blend of resin and oil became known as *varnish* and further developments led to longer-lasting 'enamel' or 'hard gloss' paints. Another type that has become increasingly popular in recent years is *emulsion* paints, in which the vehicle is a suspension or dispersion of a material such as polyvinyl acetate in water.

A widely used alternative to linseed oil, when the price is favourable, is soya bean oil. The resulting films show a much reduced tendency to yellow on exposure to air and moisture, and are therefore favoured for white and pastel colours. Other non-yellowing oils sometimes used are those extracted from the seeds of plants such as the tobacco, the safflower, the sunflower, and the poppy—a traditional favourite for artists' oil colours.

Resins and pigments The use of natural resins such as Congo copal in coatings is of great antiquity but of little importance today. For the past 30 years or so the paint industry has widely used synthetic oil-modified *alkyd* resins (see PLASTICS) which are essentially derived from the reaction of *glycerol* with *phthalic anhydride*. Alkyd resins may also be modified with other synthetic *monomers* (single molecules) to give, for example, the *alkyd-melamine* finishes used for several years by parts of the British motor industry.

Recent years have seen increasing use by the paint industry of other types of synthetic resins. *Acrylic* finishes based on POLYMERS such as *polymethyl methacrylate* are used in several countries in durable building paints and vehicle finishes. *Epoxy* resins, typically derived from *bisphenol* and *epichlorhydrin,* are probably best known for their use in ADHESIVES but are also used in corrosion-resistant coatings. Another category of growing importance is the *polyurethane* resins based on *tolylene di-isocyanate* and used in tough coatings. The continuing use of one natural resin, *nitrocellulose* (in a low nitrogen content form), in furniture lacquers and related finishes should not be overlooked.

For many years the principal white pigments were white LEAD (*basic lead carbonate*), *zinc oxide* and *lithopone* (a mixture of *zinc sulphide* and *barium sulphate*). These have now been almost entirely superseded on grounds of opacity, hiding power and toxicity by *titanium dioxide,* used in one of its three crystalline forms known as *rutile.* This is because rutile is free from the defect of the *anatase* crystalline form which causes paints to 'chalk' (lose gloss by developing a loose powdery surface). The paint industry consumes about 65% of the growing world output of the pigment.

In corrosion-resistant primers for iron and steel, red lead continues to be of prime importance. *Lead chromes* are widely used for yellow and orange shades, and in combination with blue pigments as the basis for greens. *Cadmium sulphide* has long been used as an artists' yellow, while metallic aluminium, zinc and lead have specialized uses.

All the pigments mentioned so far are of inorganic or mineral origin. Largely as a result of demand from the textile industry, a wide range of organic pigments is now available and finding increasing application in paints. Of particular interest are the metal-complex pigments such as the blue *copper phthalocyanine.* Another organic pigment is carbon black, derived from vegetable or mineral sources.

Paintmaking Manufacture of paints—the dispersion of a pigment in a vehicle—requires two kinds of movement. These are squeezing and rubbing, or in technical language *pressure* and *shear.* Early artists mixed their paints between glass or granite surfaces in a simple *muller* operated by hand. The first mechanized milling devices were two flat stones one on top of the other, the top one rotating and the bottom one fixed. An improvement on this flat stone mill was the cone mill and other types, some of which require the charge to be pre-mixed.

A widely used unit is the triple roll mill. In a typical installation the rolls are of 12 inch (30.5 cm) diameter and 30 inch (76 cm) long. They rotate at different speeds, the front rolls being fastest. A typical speed ratio is 1:3:9, the back roll

Top left: iron oxide is used in numerous kinds of paints. Other metal compounds important to the paint industry include compounds of lead, zinc, cadmium, copper and titanium.

Centre left: one of the main stages of paint manufacture is the dispersal of the pigment within the base liquid. This is commonly done in a roll mill like this one, the paint being removed from the front roller by a scraper blade.

Left: mixing the powdered pigment into the base.

Top right: samples of paint being exposed to ultra-violet light for two weeks to test colour fastness. This test exposes the samples to the equivalent of six months' sunlight.

Right: hand grinding a paint sample in the laboratory to check that the colour balance is correct before large-scale production begins.

moving at about 30 revs/min. The speed differences provide the rubbing and squeezing actions and also give a more evenly spread film. Extra shearing effect is produced in some mills by a sideways sliding motion. A scraper blade removes the paste from the front roller, when it may be ready for packing or for further thinning.

Many paintmakers use various sizes of ball mills, which can produce well-finished gloss paints with a minimum of supervision. The machine consists of a rotating cylinder which contains steel or porcelain balls or flint pebbles in quantity sufficient to occupy about 45% of the total volume. The actual space occupied is about half the apparent space and it is in the interstices that the paint is milled. The optimum point charge is therefore about 20% of the total volume, while a typical milling cycle occupies about 16 hours (that is, overnight).

A logical development from the ball mill is the modern sand mill, in which the speed of rotation is no longer limited by the centrifugal action of the grinding media. A sand mill consists essentially of a vertical cylinder containing sand of very small particle size or fine glass beads (*ballotini*), driven at high speed by a multi-disc impeller. A pump forces the pre-mixed paste of pigment and vehicle through a non-return valve into the milling area, where dispersion takes place by the rubbing of the paste between the fine particles of sand. The product is discharged through a fine wire mesh to retain the sand.

A notable feature of the sand mill is that it allows continuous operation. Paint manufacture has traditionally been a batch process, but large modern plants now operate on at least a semi-continuous basis for the most popular finishes and colours.

Another modern development is pigments which can be dispersed by mixers with specially designed blades rotating at very high speeds. In these high speed impeller mills, dispersion is again effected by attrition of the pigment aggregates and the consistency achieved may be fairly high.

Health and fire hazards Many of the materials used in paint manufacture are potentially hazardous if mishandled, but the risks are generally well understood and only elementary precautions are required of the user. Among pigments, the compounds of lead and other heavy metals have attracted particular notice because of the hazard to young children with the habit of chewing or sucking flakes of old paint. As noted above, lead pigments are now little used in decorative paints, but some countries have organized action to remove or cover up old lead-based coatings. It should be understood, however, that a small proportion of lead compounds is necessary for the rapid drying of modern paints and could only be completely eliminated at substantial cost in both price and performance. Appreciable levels of lead continue to be used in industrial finishes, where application by spraying is subject to control.

The solvent benzene is now rarely used because of danger to the lungs. Precautions are necessary with chlorinated solvents, and adequate ventilation is recommended with all spraying operations. It is also often advisable to avoid contact with the skin or eyes.

Certain specialized materials present unusual hazards. Thus nitrocellulose (another form of which is also known as gun-

Below: the 'make-up' stage of paint manufacture, in which the final additives, colour and tinting are added to the paint, and final quality control checks are carried out.

cotton) is classified as an EXPLOSIVE, while the recently intro-duced powder coatings ('dry paints') are potentially capable of giving rise to dust explosions.

Most organic substances are combustible, that is, they will inflame if heated strongly enough. The *flashpoint,* which indicates the degree of flammability of a solvent, is the lowest temperature at which the vapour collected in a closed space ignites on the introduction of a small flame. The precautions to be observed depend on the flashpoint and may involve the use of flameproof electrical equipment. Particular care may also be necessary in storage and waste disposal.

Pollution control In recent years industry as a whole has become increasingly conscious of its responsibility to avoid damage to the environment. This had led, in the paint industry, to close control of solid and liquid wastes. There has been some interest in the recycling of solvents, or their elimination in solventless coatings or powder coatings. There has also been a marked trend to water-based coatings and much effort has been devoted to the search for a full gloss emulsion paint.

A side effect of pollution control has been some scarcity of titanium dioxide. The widely used sulphate process for its manufacture gives rise to large quantities of coloured effluent

Left: filling paint cans. The paint is fed into the machine through pneumatically controlled valves, and dispensed into the cans which are then fitted with lids and packed.

Below: spraying a car body with acrylic enamel paint. Before the enamel is applied the body is coated with primer by a process in which the car is negatively charged and the primer is positively charged, the paint being deposited on the body electrostatically.

and some countries have restricted output until steps are taken to avoid damage to the environment. Carbon black is another important material subject to control on ecological grounds.

Recent developments For many years the most popular methods for applying paints were brushing, dipping and spraying. The last decade has seen widespread adoption by the motor and other industries of the *electrodeposition* or *electropainting* process, which involves passing an electric current between the metal article to be coated and the tank in which it is immersed.

Drying methods have progressed from natural evaporation of solvents, through forced drying in heated ovens to *radiation curing,* whereby specially formulated coatings 'set' in a fraction of a second under the influence of INFRA-RED or ULTRA-VIOLET radiation.

Another modern development is *coil coating,* in which acrylic, epoxy and other finishes are roller coated on to continuous steel strip before fabrication into building cladding, caravans or domestic appliances.

The modern paint industry is firmly based on scientific principles and employs all the techniques known to the chemical industry as a whole. Computers are employed in the complicated area of colour measurement and colour matching, notably on the numerous and frequently changing colours used by car manufacturers. International standardization of test methods, for example on accelerated weathering, is well advanced, while the European Economic Community has drafted a directive on the labelling of paints.

PAINTING RESTORATION (see picture restoration)

PANTOGRAPH

A pantograph is an engineering device which takes advantage of the properties of the *parallelogram*. A parallelogram is a four-sided geometrical figure having opposite sides and opposite angles which are equal. If one angle of such a figure is made larger, the opposite angle must be made larger by the same amount, and the other two angles must be made smaller by a proportional amount. A pantograph is simply a parallelogram with hinges at the corners so that it can be freely flexed.

On electric traction railroad cars which collect the current from overhead wires, the device which does the collecting is called a pantograph. The contact strip which slides on the wire is mounted on a diamond-shaped construction which can expand and contract vertically to make allowance for small variations in the height of the wire above the rails.

For accurately copying maps, drawings and so forth, especially to a different scale, a pantograph may be used. For this purpose the pantograph will be a flat construction of strips of wood or metal with holes drilled in them so that the position of the pivots can be changed, thus changing the amount of enlargement being done. The instrument is obsolete nowadays as a technical aid, but is an amusing toy.

Pantographs in series can be used to make several copies of a drawing at once, all the same size or in different scales. Pantographs in series are also used for reaching tongs, to mount a telephone on the wall, or anywhere a connection of variable length is required across a short distance. Other uses of a pantograph are as part of a power-operated railway freight van unloader, for reaching into the van, and as the part of a mechanical embroidery frame which determines the position of the ground fabric in relation to the needles.

Above: the pantograph device which collects current from the wire to drive an electric train. The parallelogram arrangement allows the collecting shoe to be moved straight up and down without altering the angle at which it touches the wire.

Below: a pantograph being used to copy a drawing of the letter A. In this case the copy will be twice the size of the original; the device can be adjusted for different ratios by moving pivots.